Ethics and Professionalism
in Engineering

Ethics and

in

MURRAY I. MANTELL

The Macmillan Company, New York

Professionalism
Engineering

Chairman, Department of Civil Engineering, University of Miami, Coral Gables, Florida

Collier-Macmillan Limited, London

Preface

This book has been written as a reference guide for the fuller appreciation of the philosophy, methodology, influence, and ideals of the practice of engineering. As a text it is aimed toward assisting the senior engineering student in the transition from the undergraduate school to professional practice and/or the graduate school. It may have potential application in courses having such titles as Professional Seminar, Professional Practice, Projects, Senior Report, Engineering Communications, or as a supplement for Contracts and Specifications.

Chapter 1 illustrates the broad methodologies of science and engineering and their major component concepts including deduction, induction, theories, causes, purpose, and metaphysics. The many books which have been written on the philosophy of science generally seem to have ignored the fact that there is a difference between the scientific method and the methodology (analysis, design, production) of engineering. These differences are brought out in the chapter.

The major theme of the text is built around an affirmation that engineering is a profession, and that a principal distinguishing factor between a profession and an occupation is the primary objective of service to humanity. Professionalism has, in large part, been advanced by means of canons and codes of ethics. Ethics is correspondingly used as a principal vehicle for accomplishing the goals of this text. An attempt has been made to treat ethics as more than a set of rules or a catalog of acts. A selected outline of the historical development of ethical thought is presented in Chapter

2. Chapter 3 illustrates the solution of problems in ethics by applying ethical principles in a methodology similar to that in which physical principles are used to solve engineering problems related to the *material* needs of man.

Chapter 4 traces the historical development of the engineering profession to its present organization and relation to society including registration requirements, employment practices, specialization, professionalism, and the concept of creative service.

Chapter 5 contains important reference material on information retrieval and documentation for engineering writing. The chapter is pointed particularly toward guidance in writing for technical journals and speaking at professional meetings. These media of communication should be furthered by encouraging students to participate in competitions sponsored by student chapters of our various engineering societies. This college experience in communication generally demonstrates that, when a worthwhile project is completed in professional practice, it is not an imposing task to present the results of this work to the profession.

Continuation of education is a problem which faces the engineer at all levels of the profession. Chapter 6 discusses this problem and its potential solution through self-study, formal training programs, and graduate studies.

The Humanistic-Social Research Project of 1956 sponsored by the American Society for Engineering Education reiterated the goals presented earlier by the Hammond Report. These goals were stated in terms of competences it was believed the humanities and social sciences could help the student acquire:

1. An understanding of the evolution of the social organization within which we live and the influence of science and engineering on its development.
2. The ability to recognize and make a critical analysis of a problem involving social and economic elements, to arrive at an intelligent opinion about it, and to read with discrimination and purpose toward these ends.
3. The ability to organize thoughts logically and to express them lucidly and convincingly in oral and written English.
4. An acquaintance with some of the great masterpieces of litera-

ture and an understanding of their setting in and influence on
civilization.

5. The development of moral, ethical and social concepts essential
to a satisfying personal philosophy, to a career consistent with
the public welfare and to a sound professional attitude.

6. The attainment of an interest and pleasure in these pursuits
and thus of an inspiration to continue study.

Topics have been included in this text which would hopefully
contribute to each of the six goals of the Hammond Report. These
topics may also comprise a course which embodies the engineering
faculties' contribution towards integration of the humanities-social
studies sequence required in each engineering curriculum. Such
topics, taught by engineering faculty, would tend to give the engineering senior a more positive appreciation of the place and value
of humanities-social studies in his career.

Traditionally, engineering has been concerned primarily with
the application of the natural sciences and mathematics, to meeting the material needs of man. A final goal of this text, in demonstrating the application of an adaptation of the methodology of
engineering to solving individual ethical problems, is to help pre-
dispose the engineering profession to extend its field of application, to exert greater influence in the solution of broad social
problems. The rapid and almost miraculous success of engineering
in meeting man's material wants leads the author to believe there
is great promise that engineers can help fill the partial vacuum of
leadership which has resulted, through the centuries, in relatively
little progress in man's treatment of man.

The author wishes to express his appreciation to the many individuals who have reviewed the manuscript and offered suggestions including W. Chang, J. H. Clouse, W. J. Fogarty, M. M.
Gaynor, G. Mayer, N. S. Pallot, H. F. Pierce, M. E. Reeder, N.
Schuck, E. W. Schuh, R. G. Spicher, J. A. Stevens, E. L. Wiener,
T. A. Weyher, and H. A. B. Wiseman; L. Snayd for the typing of
the manuscript; and to his wife, Rose, for her encouragement and
forbearance during the many months of writing.

M. I. MANTELL
February, 1964

Table of Contents

4. The Engineer and Society

5. Engineering Communications

6. Continuation of Education

CHAPTER 1

The Philosophy of Engineering

1-1. INTRODUCTION. A great many books have been written on the philosophy of science. These books usually attempt to show the past links between science and philosophy; and generally arrive at conclusions that science and philosophy have diverged, and that modern scientists have been narrowly concerned only with seeking truth to the neglect of the way these truths have been broadly interpreted or used. Writers on the philosophy of science have ordinarily included the engineer in the broad category of scientists. Whereas many conclusions, including the above, would probably apply to the engineer as well as the physicist, chemist, or biologist, there are a number of factors which are unique to the engineer. Because of these unique factors it has been considered preferable to call this chapter the philosophy of engineering.

An understanding of the philosophy of engineering should make clearer the relative positions and respective general responsibilities of the scientist, technician, and engineer. Most important, an understanding of metaphysics, causes, purposes and theories as parts of a total methodology of engineering should make each individual more competent to guide his professional work both in relation to himself and in possible extensions which may attempt to guide the destiny of others.

1-2. METAPHYSICS. The foundation for all scientific and engineering endeavour is generally considered to lie in the field of metaphysics. Metaphysics may be defined as the systematic

1

study of the fundamentals relating to the ultimate nature of reality and of human knowledge. It thus falls into two divisions, namely, Ontology—the systematic study of the ultimate problems of Being or Reality; and Epistemology—the systematic study of the ultimate problems of human knowledge. Some writers use Metaphysics as being synonymous with Ontology; others make it synonymous with Epistemology. The preference of this text is to consider Ontology a pseudo-science and to use Collingwood's definition: "Metaphysics is the science which deals with the pre-suppositions underlying ordinary scientific thinking." (1:11)

Ontology depends essentially upon analogical inference and logical argument as in the famous argument on the existence of God, Paley's Watch (4:5-44):

"But suppose I had found a *watch* upon the ground . . . the inference, we think, is inevitable; that the watch must have had a maker, . . . who formed it for the purpose which we find it actually to answer; who comprehended its construction, and designed its use. Nor would it, I apprehend, weaken the conclusion, that we had never seen a watch made: that we had never known an artist capable of making one; that we were altogether incapable of executing such a piece of workmanship ourselves, or of understanding in what manner it was performed; . . . every indication of contrivance, every manifestation of design, which existed in the watch, exists in the works of nature, of being greater and more, and that in a degree which exceeds all computation. . . . to support the conclusion which we draw from it, as to the necessity of an intelligent Creator."

Some will argue that they can accept as existing only that which is physically evident or measurable. But even that which appears physically evident is an ontological problem, for it is doubtful that one can "prove" that even that which is seen exists. We often speak of hallucinations and dreams which reveal objects one later concludes had no existence except in the mind of the dreamer. Therefore, it may be argued that all that we see may also exist only in the mind. Similarly, if an individual wished to believe that there was no life anywhere except on earth, it is unlikely that we could "prove" it otherwise, even if the converse were a reality.

Thus, if it were claimed that communications were actually received from outer space, he could say it was only a claim and a misrepresentation. If he were actually shown a strange people who did the communicating, he could say they came from some previously hidden recess of the earth. If these strange people actually took him to their planet, he could claim they put him under a hypnotic spell which made it so appear. Thus, it appears impossible to "prove" that there are any realities; and it is also possible to accept some and disclaim others, with neither category capable of proof.

The presuppositions, or assumptions, which underlie thinking are of much more concern to the engineer and scientist and have far greater implication than Ontology. All assumptions are presuppositions; but all presuppositions are not assumptions. A person who makes an assumption is making a presupposition about which he is *aware*. He is also aware that, if he were to so choose, he could make a different assumption. However, a supposition may be made *unawares*, without consciousness of the possibility that others might have been made instead.

"I see a piece of string. I find myself thinking, 'that is a clothes-line,' meaning that it was put there to hang clothes on. When I decide that it was put there for that purpose I am presupposing that it was put there for some purpose. Only if that presupposition is made does the question arise, what purpose? If that presupposition was not made, if for example I had thought the line came there by accident, that question would not have arisen, and the situation in which I think 'that is a clothes-line' would not have occurred." (1:21)

The orderly, systematic thinker is aware of his presuppositions (assumptions).

"In unscientific thinking our thoughts are coagulated into knots and tangles; we fish up a thought out of our minds like an anchor foul of its own cable, hanging upside down and draped in seaweed with shellfish sticking to it, and dump the whole thing on the deck quite pleased with ourselves for having got it up at all. Thinking scientifically means disentangling all this mess, and reducing a knot of thoughts in which everything sticks together anyhow to a system or series of thoughts in which thinking the thoughts is at the same time thinking of the connections between them." (1:22-23)

A presupposition or assumption may be true or false, or we may not know whether it is true or false. For example, when we ask for a receipt for a sum of money paid, we may do this on the presupposition that the other party is capable of being dishonest, although we do not know for a fact whether or not he will be dishonest.

The proper place of metaphysics is not to decide which presuppositions are true, but to find out what presuppositions have been made in a particular instance. Unless we recognize and agree upon the same assumptions there can be no verification of a theory or no satisfactory application of an equation.

Every question is based upon one or more presuppositions. If the one who asks has presuppositions which are different from the one who answers, there is no real communication. Thus if a question is asked: "Can we move this weight?", the answer might be "no" if there is a presupposition that we two have to do it manually; however, the answer would be "yes" if there is a presupposition that mechanical equipment can be used. Much of the trouble and confusion in the world is due to similar unstated and unclear presuppositions.

Whenever we use an instrument to make a measurement we presuppose (assume) that it has not changed since the last time it was calibrated. The instrument may be incorrect now, even though it was calibrated only seconds prior. At best, we can only be "certain" that the instrument was satisfactory (assuming the calibration equipment is correct) at the instant of calibration; and we cannot be "certain" of its calibration at any other instant. The above is a good example of a very practical application of metaphysical thinking, in that such thinking clearly indicates the importance of verifying observations or measurements by two or more completely independent means.

It might be worth investigating whether or not metaphysics, the ability to recognize our presuppositions, is the major difference between the intelligence (reasoning) of humans and the intelligence (reasoning) of the other animals. The relatively great achievements in science and engineering may be largely due to the workers in each field being able and willing to agree upon basic assumptions.

1-3. CAUSE. Many scientists and metaphysicians claim that every event has a cause, and that the cause of an event is a previous event. Thus, the cause of poor concrete is too much water in the mix; or the cause of a short-circuit is frayed insulation, the cause of the frayed insulation is the wind, the cause of the wind is . . . , ad infinitum·to the "absolute" cause. Other scientists and metaphysicians claim that nothing has a cause; and still others claim that some things have causes and others have no causes.

It is doubtful if we can ever find the absolute causes of the universe, or the absolute causes of any event, even if they do exist; nor need these absolute causes be of particular concern to the engineer or scientist. For example, if an engineer were to come forth and declare in great triumph: "I have discovered the cause of gravity," the profession would be unlikely to pay near as much attention as to a proclamation: "I am able to both produce and prevent gravity." This demonstrates an important principle: *we are interested in causes of a given thing primarily in the sense that the cause is one of its conditions which we are able to produce or prevent.*

An example is adapted from Collingwood: A car skids and overturns while going around a curve. From the driver's point of view, and ability to prevent future accidents, the cause was excessive speed and the remedy is more careful driving. From the highway engineer's point of view, and ability to prevent, the cause (or condition) might be improper super elevation of the road. From the auto manufacturers' point of view, and ability to prevent, the cause (condition) might have been a center of gravity that was too high. If they all make the contributions that they are able, considerable progress will be made toward preventing future accidents. Conversely, if each felt that the cause or condition was one that only someone else could prevent, the result would be that nothing would be done.

One of the great problems of our society is that too many are always asking: "Why don't *they* do something about it?," instead of seeking the causes or conditions which they themselves can make contributions towards preventing or producing. We are all capable, at least in some small way, of treating the causes of most things for which we have a concern; and this is our obligation—not someone elses.

1-4. LAWS AND THEORIES. At best we can say the laws of nature describe what actually happens. We cannot be certain that the sun will rise everyday throughout eternity. We can only observe that it rises today, and that it rises tomorrow, and the next day, etc. Only a finite number can be observed. Max Planck, the founder of the first Quantum theory, stated: "We have no right to assume any physical laws exist; or if they have existed up to now, that they will continue to exist in a similar manner in the future."

Particularly since the introduction of Einstein's Theory of Relativity, there has arisen great doubt that man ever will determine an absolute law of nature. Scientific progress has seen the gradual evolving of "laws" and theories which account for and predict a greater and greater scope of reality—but not all of reality. Our "laws" and theories are only approximately correct, and this only within a limited range. Our progress has been in evolving theories which improve the accuracy, increase the range, and account for some of the exceptions of prior theories.

Historically we can look back and see that scientists and engineers have been continually using "incorrect" theories in their work. This may be best demonstrated by a brief review of the evolution of the oldest of the formal sciences, astronomy. Records in China, Egypt, and Babylon indicate astronomical studies dating prior to 3000 B.C. The relatively precise orientation of the Pyramids demonstrates that, even with the presupposition of the flatness of the earth, these early theories were able to account for and predict reasonably well many of the observed phenomena. Ancient astronomy culminated with the geocentric theory of Hipparchus and Ptolemy, respectively about 130 B.C. and A.D. 140. The geocentric theory presupposed that the earth was a fixed sphere at the center of the universe, and that all the celestial bodies moved with uniform motion in perfect circles. This theory applied geometry and trigonometry most skillfully and, where necessary, introduced combinations of concentric and eccentric circles with appropriate diameters, and epicycles (a circle moving around the circumference of another circle—see Fig. 1-1). The

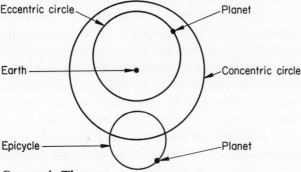

Fig. 1-1 Geocentric Theory

geocentric theory explained and predicted observed phenomena so well that the theory remained relatively unquestioned until the time of Copernicus in the sixteenth century. The heliocentric theory of Copernicus, presupposing the sun to be the fixed center of the universe, explained many of the exceptions of the geocentric theory, and approximated more accurately the observed phenomena. The heliocentric theory has now been superseded by the theory of relativity, and its space—time continuum, which explains still more of the exceptions and extends the degree of accuracy with which we can predict observed phenomena.

Coming closer to engineering, we have been applying Euclidian geometry (e.g., the axiom the sum of the angles of a triangle equals 180°), Newtonian Mechanics (e.g., force equals mass times acceleration), and the wave theory of light (e.g., application to optical lenses); yet the theory of relativity and the quantum theory have shown all of these to be "incorrect." The scientists and engineers thus appear to be always in the middle of a dilemma, of having to work with "incorrect" theories. A sage answer to this apparent dilemma may be found in the writings of Ptolemy: "In seeking to explain phenomena, we should adopt the simplest possible hypothesis, provided it is not contradicted in any important respect by the observations."

The criteria for choice of a theory, or method of analysis and design, should include a consideration of the agreement with observation and its relative simplicity. It is doubtful if any theory can give us complete agreement with all our observations. The engineer must use his best judgment in selecting a theory (or method of analysis and design) by compromising between one which is more in agreement with observations but complicated, and another less in agreement with observations but simpler.

An example of this may be illustrated by our currently used methods for the design of rivets. A riveted connection, as shown in Fig. 1-2, is designed by using the equation $f = F/A$, where f is

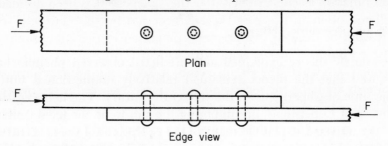

Fig. 1-2 **Riveted Connection**

the stress, F is the force, and A is the area under stress. The method of design and derivation of the equation includes amongst its assumptions: that rivets exist, the force is static and the body in equilibrium and "at rest," the force is applied at the centroid of the resisting areas, the body is "rigid" (will not buckle) yet elastic, the material is homogeneous and isotropic, and the areas of each rivet are equally stressed. In this instance it is evident that the force is not applied at the centroid of the resisting areas; and even if we could apply the load at the centroid, we would find (amongst other variances from the assumptions that the stress in each unit of area was not equal. However, the method does give, in a simple manner, reasonably satisfactory results when riveted connections are to be designed. Up to now, any methods which are more in agreement with observations, or the facts, have been considered too complex for practical use.

1-5. PURPOSE. Thus our theory, or method of analysis and design, must be efficient in predicting future observable facts upon the basis of facts observed in the past. In selecting a theory we chose an instrument which can with efficiency and reasonable correctness serve a "purpose." Consideration of the "purpose" cannot be separated from correctness and simplicity; and undoubtedly, "purpose" should be the major factor. In designing an airplane the "purpose" may be speed in transportation; it may be safety in transportation; it may be the destruction of other men; or it may be a compromise between these. The "purpose" of a building may be for a hospital or a warehouse. Engineering can function efficiently only after the "purpose" has been decided. All too often in the past the engineer has let the "purpose" of his work be decided by others. Participation in the establishment of the "purpose" of his work with material things of the universe is one place where the engineer can, today, begin to make inroads towards applying the social and behavioral sciences for the benefit of man.

1-6. DEDUCTION AND INDUCTION. *Deduction* is defined as a form of reasoning by which a specific fact or conclusion is derived or inferred from a general principle or theory. Thus from the theory: "the sun rises every day," we can deduce that the sun will rise today, tomorrow, the next day, etc.; that is, we deduce that it will rise each of these specific days. The engineer most commonly uses the process of deduction in his applications of mathematics. Thus, solution of the general equation $f = F/A$ allows us to deduce the specific value of f from given specific values of F and A. One should not infer that the mathematical process itself is clear-cut and self-evident. For a most interesting enlightenment on the metaphysics of mathematics, the reader is strongly urged to study discussions on this subject such as the one by Kemeny. (2)

Induction is defined as a form of reasoning by which a general principle or theory is derived or inferred from a number of specific facts. Thus, from observing that the sun rises today, tomorrow, the next day, etc., we can induce the theory that "The sun rises every day." The process of induction has been classified into a number of methods. Some of the more important of these methods include: the *Method of Difference* involving observations or experiments which show that the elimination of a certain factor or antecedent is followed by the nonappearance of the phenomena concerned, with all other relevant factors remaining unchanged; the *Method of Concomitant Variations* involving observations or experiments which show that a quantitative change in a certain factor or antecedent is followed by a quantitative change in the phenomena concerned, with all other relevant factors remaining unchanged; and the *Statistical Method* involving a study of correlations and associations of observed facts.

The process of induction, of leading to generalization from specific facts, can all too readily lead to rash generalizations. Thus, superstitions may have evolved as generalizations where certain events have been observed to occur at the same time, or in rapid succession. Similarly, reckless generalizations are made about the characteristics of whole peoples, after a superficial acquaintance with a very few representatives. These dangers can be avoided by recognizing that the inductive process is only one part of the orderly, systematic total approach which is needed. This total approach, considering factors and processes additional to those previously mentioned in this chapter, is discussed in the next section as the *Methodologies of Science and Engineering*.

1-7. METHODOLOGIES OF SCIENCE AND ENGINEERING. The flow chart of Fig. 1-3 is an attempt to demonstrate an orderly, systematic total approach, or

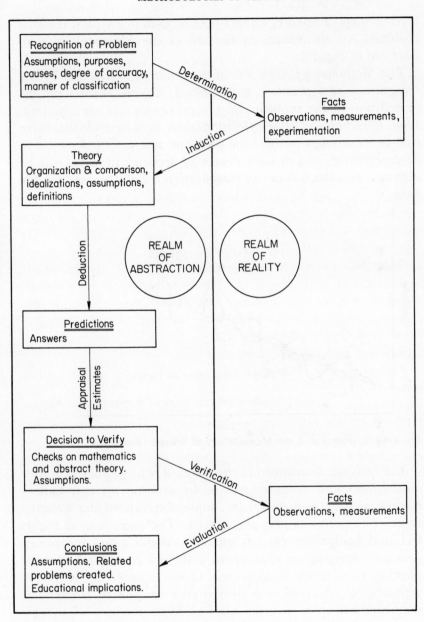

Fig. 1-3   Methodology of Science (Research)

Methodology of Science, which might be used in a typical research problem. An elementary application of the Methodology is illustrated in Fig. 1-4.

The Methodology starts out in the realm of abstraction by the *recognition of a problem to be solved.* Closely allied with the recognition of the problem are the previously discussed *assumptions, purposes,* and *causes.* Decisions then must be made that there will be an attempt to solve the problem, that certain *facts* are to be determined, and to what *degree of accuracy* the facts will be obtained or what *manner of classification* should be used for the facts.

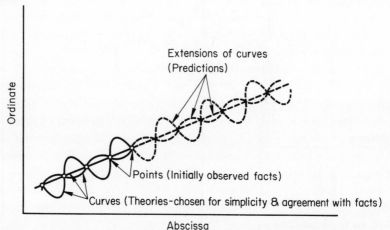

Fig. 1-4 Application of the Methodology of Science (Research)

The facts are determined in the realm of reality either by *simple observations and measurements* or by *experimentation.* Experimentation is distinguished from simple observations and measurements by *control* of the phenomena. The mere use of highly technical equipment, even at specially suitable times and places, does not constitute an experiment if there is no control over the phenomena observed or measured. In the example of Figure 1-4, a number of observed or measured facts are plotted as circles at the lower left.

Moving back into the realm of abstraction of Fig. 1-3, the facts may be *organized* and *compared* and a *theory* evolved by the process of *induction*. Usually in evolving the theory it is propitious to make some *idealizations*. The intricacies of many complex problems make it desirable to simplify certain aspects by disregarding or by setting up ideal forms or limits. Thus in many practical problems we work with "frictionless" motion; or in the case of structures we idealize into the simple line form of the "free-body diagram."

Referring back to Fig. 1-4, notice that an infinite number of curves (theories), three of which are shown, can be drawn (induced) through the given points (facts). Whereas all of the theories may approximate the given facts, the one which both gives a good approximation and is relatively simple (in this instance, the straight line) is the one that should be chosen. Readings may now be taken from the extended curves (deduction) to predict a series of new specific facts.

Before there can be *deduction* or use of the *predictions,* it is usually necessary to consider any new assumptions in the theory and to set up clear rules of interpretation or *definitions* of all elements of the theory and terms in equations. After *checks of mathematics and abstract theory,* new *assumptions* and an *appraisal* of reasonableness of *answers* and *estimates* of costs and time involved in checking should determine whether or not there is a *decision to verify* against the actual conditions. The *verification* is made by taking additional *measurements* and *observations* of the *facts,* back in the realm of reality.

The final *evaluation* is made, in the realm of abstraction, after the verification has been terminated. Here new *assumptions* are probably needed to arrive at *conclusions* as to whether or not the problem has been solved satisfactorily, what *related problems* have been created, and the *educational implications* (the obligations to report the findings to the profession).

A problem involving engineering analysis, design and production or construction would follow a methodology very similar to that used in research, as previously discussed. The differences may be noted by comparing Fig. 1-5 and Fig. 1-3. The first point of departure is that, after the necessary initial facts are acquired, an

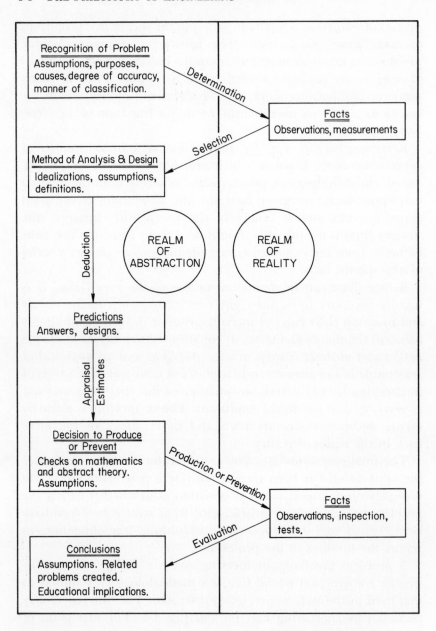

Fig. 1-5 Methodology of Engineering (Analysis, Design & Production)

existing and known *method of analysis and design* is *selected* for use, instead of induction of a new theory as is done in research. It is also appropriate to mention at this time that almost all engineering analysis can be broken down into a three-step procedure (or cyclic use thereof): (a) Idealization of the physical system (e.g., free-body diagram, electrical circuit diagram); (b) Mathematical model of the physical system (e.g., $\Sigma M = O$, $E = I/R$; (c) Solution of the mathematical model (deduction) to obtain the answers (predictions). (3:4-6) Appraisal and estimates related to the *design* then should determine whether or not there is a *decision to produce or prevent,* differing from the decision to verify the predictions of the theory evolved from research. The final difference is in the process of *production or prevention,* instead of verification, during which there may be *inspection,* or *tests* may be made at completion of the process.

1-8. VALUE JUDGMENTS. At many stages in a particular application of the Methodologies of Science and Engineering value judgments are required. These may include the decision that the problem is or is not worth solving, decisions on purposes and causes, establishment of assumptions, decision as to which theory is the best compromise between accuracy and simplicity, decisions as to what degree of accuracy and factor of safety shall be used, decisions as to the idealizations to be used, appraisal of the predictions, and the final evaluation of results. Scientific instruments can be used to make clear-cut observations of facts, and mathematics can be used to obtain clear-cut answers from an equation; but neither instruments nor mathematics can, at least at this time, be used to make value judgments. Instruments and mathematics can present the alternatives clearly outlined, free from emotional slogans, and free from superstitious representations; but they cannot decide what is good, simple, satisfactory, necessary, desirable, etc.

The stages of a problem which involve assumptions and value judgments are the ones which usually designate the line of separation between the work of the professional engineer and the work of the technician. No equation, no handbook table is valid, except within a relatively small range of circumstances which are limited by the assumptions. There must be no blind substitution in equations or blind reading of answers out of a handbook; these answers must be used with discrimination for the class of limited applications. Referring to the flow charts of Figs. 1-3 and 1-5, the usual place of the technician may be seen—performing those tasks which require no assumptions and no value judgments. Thus the technician will be limited to gathering the original facts, performing simple observations and measurements, performing routine experiments, verifying the facts, controlling production by inspection and tests, and obtaining the predictions (answers and designs) by mere substitution in formulas or readings from handbooks (which are designated to be applicable).

The professional engineer must necessarily be concerned with the total methodologies of science and engineering. The value judgments he makes are, largely, conscious or unconscious (and preferably conscious) applications of the social and behavioral sciences. The foundations of value judgments and potential applications of the social and behavioral sciences may be found in the study of ethics; and the foundations of ethics are thereupon discussed in the next chapter.

ASSIGNMENTS

1.1 List the "assumptions" in the normal applications of the following equations:

a) $f = My/I$

b) $E = I/R$

c) $F = ma$

d) $s = \frac{1}{2} at^2$

e) $Q = vA$

f) $v = at$

g) $V_1 V_2 = T_1 T_2$

1.2 List the possible "causes" (conditions which an engineer might be able to produce or prevent) of the following:

a) A boiler explosion

b) Collapse of a bridge

c) Flooding of a river

d) Radiation contamination

e) Radio static

1.3 List possible "purposes" of the following engineering assignments and indicate how each purpose might dictate different designs.

- *a*) To design a vehicle capable of traveling on either land or water;
- *b*) To design an instrument which measures and isolates colors;
- *c*) To design equipment which will separate solid particles in a gaseous mixture;
- *d*) To design an instrument which measures the vibration frequency of sounds.

1.4 For the following designs, show on a flow chart, similar to that of Fig. 1-5, what is to be used or determined (non-quantitatively) at each stage, including theories (equations) and particularly where and what assumptions and value judgments are to be made:

- *a*) Design and install a swing to be used by children under 10 years of age;
- *b*) Design and install a buzzer to signal from one room to an adjacent room;
- *c*) Design and install a unit which would keep a copper rod constantly at 212° F.

BIBLIOGRAPHY

(1) COLLINGWOOD, R. G. *An Essay on Metaphysics.* London: Oxford University Press, 1940. 354 pp.

(2) KEMENY, JOHN G. *A Philosopher Looks at Science.* Princeton, N.J.: D. Van Nostrand Company, Inc., 1959. 273 pp.

(3) MANTELL, M. I. and MARRON, J. F. *Structural Analysis.* New York: The Ronald Press Company, 1962. 422 pp.

(4) PALEY, WILLIAM. *Natural Theology.* Boston: Gould and Lincoln, 1854. 421 pp.

SUGGESTED ADDITIONAL READING

FRANK, PHILIPP. *Philosophy of Science,* Englewood Cliffs, N.J.: Prentice-Hall, Inc., 1957. 394 pp.

SEARLES, HERBERT L. *Logic and the Scientific Method,* 2nd ed. New York: The Ronald Press Company, 1956. 378 pp.

CHAPTER 2

Foundations of Ethics

2-1. INTRODUCTION. Most people's daily lives center on the problems of mere existence. They must work today so that they may earn money to buy food, clothing and shelter; so that they will be able to work tomorrow, so that they may earn money to be able to work the next day to earn money, to . . . , *ad infinitum.* The struggle for mere physical existence has been so severe, and still is for many, that there has been little time for thinking of anything beyond the problems of survival. But now that science and engineering have opened the way for easing the burden of survival, there is time for many more men to reflect on what there is beyond mere existence—on what is the purpose of man's existence. The scientist and engineer, as well as others, all too often are concerned with what exists or what happens and neglect completely *what matters.* The consideration of what matters, of what ought to be done, or the study of values and duty in human conduct, is the field of ethics.

Life continuously forces us to make decisions—to choose between right and wrong, to approve or disapprove. A life which is concerned primarily with mere physical existence or material comfort, without other goals or a sense of direction, tends to react by impulse, force of habit, inertia, or the flip of a coin; and when leisure comes we hear the continual cry of the unguided: "Let's do something," "Let's go somewhere." We must assume that one form of conduct may be more likely to accomplish one's purpose better than another. Ethics should show direction and the scale of values to choose those forms of conduct which tend to fulfill these purposes. Skill in solving ethical or moral problems, just as in solving engineering problems, requires intensive study and guided practice. In this brief introduction to ethics there will be an attempt to show the great wealth of knowledge in this area which has been built up over thousands of years, and to demonstrate how this may be organized and used systematically to gain a personal unity in this world of turmoil—and to make some small contribution to reducing the turmoil.

"During recent years there has been a remarkable growth of interest in moral philosophy. It would be difficult to determine the extent to which progress has been achieved in the rash of books and journal articles that have seen the light of day the last decade or so . . . excitement has been in the air and the conviction fairly widespread that progress in moral philosophy, if not actually realized, is imminent." (5:vii)

2-2. ORIGINS OF ETHICS.

Primitive man's struggles for existence necessitated certain actions which would be considered ethical in character. Hunger and thirst and the need for protection against "cold, wind and rain" were amongst the stimuli which developed the desirable attributes of industriousness and prudence. The hostility of animals and of other men demanded of those who survived that temper be replaced by self-control, gluttony and drunkeness by temperance, carelessness by competence, indifference by concern, etc.

Devotion to mate, children, family, and the advantages offered by cooperation of a close group or tribe brought about the need for development of customs or unwritten laws of proper conduct for all the members of the social group. Those tribes that developed the ability to work together had a marked advantage in their capability to both provide and protect. Thus social characteristics such as loyalty, obedience and mutual service tended to replace greed, lust, caprice and internal quarreling. Actions by one individual which were disagreeable to the tribe were readily evident in the close daily relations that existed. The non-conformist very quickly became aware of the resentment, anger, contempt, ridicule, or rebuke of the tribe. Conversely, actions considered proper and desirable were responded to promptly by praise and honor. The individual had to conform or to be ready to undergo the severe additional hazards of living alone.

As tribal groups merged to form nations they usually found that individual and different tribal customs were not satisfactory for the harmony of the entire group. Hence the ruling authority of the nation often found it desirable and necessary to establish a uniform written code which supplanted various unwritten customs of the separate tribes (e.g., the code of Hammurabi in Babylonia, the Code of Deuteronomy including the Ten Commandments, and the Code of Manu of the Hindus which amongst its detailed commandments over daily living fixed the caste system of India). Whereas many of the customs and codes were initiated with foresight and wisdom, other ruling authorities imposed generally abhorrent customs such as caste, dueling, slavery, human sacrifice, cannibalism, infanticide, and senicide (killing the elderly at a fixed age). Undoubtedly, in most of these instances, there was no valid standard of judgment nor continuous reflective thought to evaluate existing customs, to consider when a custom needed changing or if a new custom was better than the old. Customs and codes were followed by the more comprehensive legal systems of common law and statutes, representing more or less the minimum ethics which the majority of the people would accept. Here again the legal systems require a standard of judgment to evaluate where the law represents special privilege, obsolete application, or poor adjudication.

As the social community increased in size the danger from animals decreased, the struggle for existence softened, and many of the stimuli for ethical progress tended to be removed. In the crowded community it is much easier to live a life which is relatively isolated from the scrutiny of others. The criminal can hide much easier in the crowded city than was possible in the narrow confines of the tribal community. In the large community it becomes more difficult to know who is responsible for shoddy goods and many other kinds of unethical action may tend to flourish undetected. Whereas primitive man worked off his energies and thus quieted his impulses and passions, the relatively monotonous occupations of the city dweller creates restlessness and a craving for excitement which tends to breed delinquency or criminal activities.

With increasing civilization some aid to ethical progress came about by the development of that which we call conscience. Certain actions are followed by pleasure; others by pain and disaster. These experiences and the accumulated knowledge of customs, codes, and statutes are the base from which conscience develops. Conscience can be particularly valuable in an emergency, when there is no time for reflection; but just as our total memory of long past happenings is bound to be subject to error frequently, so may the part of our memory related to proper actions (conscience) be subject to frequent error. Conscience differs widely with the experiences of the individual and his reactions to his unique environment, and if the environment, customs and codes are wrong, then the base from which the conscience develops is wrong.

Evolutionary natural selection, custom, codes, conscience, and legal systems all have made contributions to ethical progress; but even our highly complex modern legal system dictates proper conduct for only a small percentage of the innumerable daily actions of the individual, and all of the above factors are subject to considerable error in their applications. The major advance in ethical progress came with the development of formalized comprehensive reflective ethical theories which were potentially applicable to every action of every individual. Some of these theories which are most well known are outlined in the following sections.

2-3. ETHICS OF ARISTOTLE. The birth of systemized reflective ethical theory is generally considered to have taken place in the time span of about 100 years between 425-325 B.C. A succession of great teachers: Socrates the teacher of Plato, and Plato the teacher of Aristotle culminated in Aristotles'

Nicomachean Ethics, (generally believed to be named in honor of his son, Nichomachus).

Aristotle seeks, initially, in his treatise to find out what is the aim or function of man, what will bring man happiness, what is the good man. He states that we speak of the aim or function of something in terms of what it is especially adapted to do. Thus, the eye is especially adapted to see, the knife is especially adapted to cut; and the "good" eye sees well, the "good" knife cuts well. The one thing that man does especially well, in comparison with plants, the horse, the ox, or other animals, is to apply rational principles to living. Thus, the aim or function of the "good" man is to seek the fullest life based on reason, on will, on virtue.

Aristotle separates man and his virtues into two parts: one part (the intellectual virtues) possesses and exercises reason, the other part (the moral virtues) is obedient to reason. The intellectual virtues owe their birth and growth to *education.* They are sought for their own sake, independent of vices to be overcome, and include art, scientific knowledge (truth), intuitive insight, and practical wisdom. The moral virtues are acquired by *training* to form habits, and are means to an end, where the end is the *good* life or happiness.

"The (moral) virtues we get by first exercising them, as also happens in the case of the arts as well. For the things we have to learn before we can do them, we learn by doing them, e.g., men become builders by building and lyre-players by playing the lyre; so too we become just by doing just acts, temperate by doing temperate acts, brave by doing brave acts." (1:348-49)

In order to make the moral virtues obedient to reason Aristotle sets down the famous doctrine of the *golden mean,* which indicates that each moral virtue is a point or mean between the extremes of excess and deficiency, with both excess and deficiency being vices.

"Drink or food which is above or below a certain amount destroys the health while that which is proportionate both produces and increases and preserves it. So too is it, then, in the case of temperance and courage and the other virtues. For the man who flees from and

fears everything and does not stand his ground against anything becomes a coward, and the man who fears nothing at all but goes to
meet every danger becomes rash; and similarly the man who indulges
in every pleasure and abstains from none becomes self-indulgent,
while the man who shuns every pleasure, as boors do, becomes in a
way insensible; temperance and courage, then are destroyed by excess
and defect, and preserved by the mean." (1:349)

Additional examples are given later in the text such as modesty is
the mean between being shameless or bashful; righteous indignation is the mean between envy and spite.

The mean or right amount will necessarily differ for each man.
The right amount of food or exercise for one man may not be
right for another man. Each man must determine the mean for
himself; these deliberations should not be based upon mere
opinion or prejudice nor the ends of desire. We deliberate not
about ends but about the means to an accepted end (e.g., a doctor
doesn't deliberate whether or not he shall heal, but only about
what means to accomplish the healing). The choice of the means
should be voluntary and determined by reason and not mere imita-
tion of another; and, most important, the choice must be possible.
That is, one may not be able to choose to be immortal; and some
things such as cruelty and evil have no mean—they already imply
vice (i.e., a little of everything is *not* acceptable).

"That moral virtue is a mean, then, and in what sense it is so, and
that it is a mean between two vices, the one involving excess, the other
deficiency, and that it is such because its character is to aim at what is
intermediate in passions and in actions, has been sufficiently stated.
Hence also it is no easy task to be good. For in everything it is no easy
task to find the middle, e.g., to find the middle of a circle is not for
everyone but for him who knows; so too, any one can get angry—that is
easy—or give or spend money; but to do this to the right person, to the
right extent, at the right time, with the right motive, and in the right
way, *that* is not for everyone, nor is it easy; wherefore goodness is
both rare and laudable and noble." (1:354-55)

The latter part of Aristotle's treatise on ethics is devoted to
detailed discussions of the intellectual virtues, some of the moral
virtues, and the concepts of justice, friendship, pleasure and

happiness. The doctrine of the *golden mean* is applied, for example, to justice as being an equality between the losses and gain to the parties involved, and to friendship as a striving for equality and reciprocity in goodwill, utility, and pleasantness.

2-4. NATURALISTIC THEORIES. The Stoic philosophers were the first to formalize an ethics which is based primarily upon an attempt to live in harmony with nature. The Stoic philosophy was founded by Zeno (about 340-265 B.C.) and took its name from the Stoa, a cloistered shelter where the followers of Zeno met for lectures and discussions. Zeno's philosophy answered particularly well the need for an inner stability which could withstand the ordeals associated with the great political and social changes which took place as the Hellenic empire disintegrated. It is a philosophy which served well both the slave, Epictetus (A.D. 60-138), and the Emperor Marcus Aurelius (A.D. 121-180).

The early Stoics identified nature, or the universe, with God, the universe being considered the material body of God. This pantheistic concept is illustrated in the writings of Marcus Aurelius:

"I am composed of the formal and the material; and neither of them will perish into non-existence, as neither of them came into existence out of non-existence. Every part of me then will be reduced by change into some part of the universe, and that again will change into another part of the universe, and so on forever. . . . Nothing happens to any man which he is not formed by nature to bear. . . . Think of the universal substance, of which thou hast a very small portion; and of universal time, of which a short and indivisible interval has been assigned to thee; and of that which is fixed by destiny, and how small a part of it thou art. . . . I am a part of the whole which is governed by nature; next, I am in a manner intimately related to the parts which are of the same kind with myself. For remembering this, inasmuch as I am a part, I shall be discontented with none of the things which are assigned to me out of the whole; for nothing is injurious to the part, if it is for the advantage of the whole." (2:271-72)

Within the pantheistic concept there may be seen the emphasis on the resignation to acceptance of God's will. The "good" man

submits to Him that orders the universe as the good citizen submits to the law of the city. Every existing thing performs a function which is necessary to the whole universe. No one should
complain of his station in life, physical attributes or deformities,
or his intellectual endowments for the world has need of just such
a person. A slave as Epictetus can fill a needed place in the universe as well as an emperor like Marcus Aurelius. Nature in her
wisdom has placed only certain things within the power and control of each man. Each man has control over his own feelings
and thoughts, but only limited control over that which affects his
body, property, reputation, etc. One should concentrate upon
what is within his own power or control and learn simply to accept
what is not in his power.

"Suppose that men kill thee, cut thee in pieces, curse thee. What
then can these things do to prevent thy mind from remaining pure,
wise, sober, just? For instance, if a man should stand by a limpid pure
spring, and curse it, the spring never ceases sending up potable water;
and if he should cast clay into it or filth, it will speedily dispense
them and wash them out, and will not be at all polluted. How then
shalt thou possess a perpetual fountain and not a mere well? By
forming thyself hourly to freedom conjoined with contentment,
simplicity, modesty." (2:290)

"There is only one way to happiness, and let this rule be ready both
in the morning and during the day and by night; the rule is not to
look toward things which are out of the power of the will, to think
that nothing is our own." (3:227)

The Stoics also attempt to tear apart false values:

"How strangely men act. They will not praise those who are living
at the same time and living with themselves; but to be themselves
praised by posterity, by those whom they have never seen or will ever
see, this they set much value on. But this is very much the same as if
thou shouldst be grieved because those who have lived before thee did
not praise thee." (2:275)

Living in conformance with nature implies according to the
rational nature of man. The Stoics agree with Aristotle in stating
that reason is the highest function of man and the life directed by

reason is the highest good of man. They accepted destiny but also assumed a man free when he brings his will into conformity with reason, and therefore in conformity with the will of God. Freedom is not then inconsistent with destiny, for destiny is the consistent and rational will of a benificent rational power directing all things toward the good. The man who does not bring his desires into harmony with reason is not free; he is the slave of appetite, passion, and environment.

"When you must write something to your friend, grammar will tell you what words to write; but whether you should write or not, grammar will not tell you. And so it is with music as to musical sounds; but whether you should sing at the present time and play on the lute, or do neither, music will not tell you. What faculty then will tell you? . . . the rational faculty; for this is the only faculty that we have received which examines itself, what it is, and what power it has, and what is the value of this gift, and examines all other faculties: for what else is there which tells us that golden things are beautiful, for they do not say so themselves . . . that . . . is the only thing which the gods have placed in our power . . . this body is not yours, but clay finely tempered." (3:105)

One might get the impression that Stoic ethics suggests the life of the recluse who attempts to be unconcerned with the world. However Stoic ethics not only says that to act against one another is contrary to nature but that each man is a brother to every man and there must be social concern.

"Never in reply to the question, to what country you belong, say that you are an Athenian or a Corinthian, but that you are a citizen of the world." (3:114)

"As to the animals which have no reason and generally all things and objects, do thou, since thou hast reason and they have none, make use of them with a generous and liberal spirit. But towards human beings, as they have reason, behave in a social spirit." (2:276)

"A branch cut off from the adjacent branch must of necessity be cut off from the whole tree also. So too a man when he is separated from another man has fallen off from the whole community. Now as to a branch, another cuts it off, but a man by his own act separates himself from his neighbor when he hates him and turns away from him, and he does not know that he has at the same time cut himself off from the whole social system." (2:303)

Amongst the well known proponents of a naturalistic type of ethics, in more modern times, is Herbert Spencer (1820-1903). Spencer's early education and endeavors were in the field of engineering; he later moved into diverse activities writing major works in such fields as education, biology, psychology, sociology, politics, general philosophy, and ethics. His writings were greatly influenced by Darwin's theory of evolution; and in ethics he considered it a major precept that man should strive for better adaptation to his environment and avoid interference with nature's laws. Ethical principles should not be derived from an authoritarian source, nor are they known intuitively. Ethical actions should be measured by the methods of science and brought into agreement with observed facts. Spencer was especially concerned with the rights of the individual, and with the necessity for non-interference on the part of government. The ethical goal of each man is to help evolve the perfect society. We should recognize that there is an absolute ethics, the rules and conduct which would apply to the perfectly good man in the perfectly good society; but since neither man nor society has reached perfection as yet, it is necessary that we use a relative ethics which is appropriate to our present stage in the process of evolution. These actions should be those which promote the longevity and security of each individual, and the general welfare of society. We should strive for equality of opportunity rather than equality of material things or of happiness. In the social state mutual aid should replace contention, and even competition should come to be a rivalry in kindness.

2-5. HEDONISTIC AND UTILITARIAN THEORIES. The hedonistic and utilitarian theories of ethics determine goodness of an act by the pleasure or happiness brought about by the act. Proponents of these theories consider pleasure and happiness as ultimate ends desired by all people. One may want money or material possessions; but these are only

to attain something else which is desired more. Pleasure is not pursued for some other end; and therefore may be considered an ultimate end and not a means to another end. Opponents of these theories point out that, even though the major pleasure theories are not narrowly oriented, the theories can easily be misinterpreted to assume that the pleasures to be sought are limited to, or primarily, individual immediate pleasures related to the physical senses.

The earliest formal hedonistic theory of ethics is generally considered to have been evolved by *Epicurus* (342-270 B.C.). Epicurus, a Greek teacher, founded a school and model community (the Garden of Epicurus) in which and his disciples lived the life which was expounded in their teaching. They were strong advocates of a simple life concerned only with essentials. They stressed that happiness can be obtained with few worldly goods, and that cultivation of vain fancies and habits of luxury cause the greatest trouble; these desires can never be satisfied. Luxuries one cannot afford will not detract from happiness if the individual will just make up his mind that he does not want them; either get what you want or stop wanting.

The Epicureans in evaluating an action placed greatest emphasis on the intensity of the pleasure. Therefore, pleasures of the mind and actions which result in the greatest amount of pleasure in one's lifetime were to take precedence over pleasures of the body and pleasures of the moment. Every action therefore must be in harmony with the ideal of a happy and complete life. Intemperance, dishonesty, and all the vices must be excluded because in terms of one's entire lifetime they would bring more pain than pleasure. Cultivation of health and friendship were considered amongst the greatest of pleasures. Also considered as an important type of pleasure was the absence of pain in the body and trouble in the soul. For example, it was considered a mistake to worry about death when it was not present; and when death comes one will not be able to worry about it. The Epicurean evaluation of happiness centered primarily on the happiness of the individual. There was no great social concern; however, they were very concerned about not interfering with others, particularly by force.

In more modern times, Jeremy Bentham (1748-1832) was amongst the first to formalize a pleasure theory with emphasis on the total effects upon society. Bentham, in his book *An Introduction to the Principles of Morals and Legislation,* presents the principle of utility which regards the essential element in ethical conduct as the tendency of an individual act to increase the amount of happiness which may be experienced by the members of society. The society he referred to is all the people affected by a particular act; and the ultimate end should be the greatest happiness for the greatest number.

Bentham devised a method for evaluating or measuring individual ethical actions which he called "a calculus of pleasures." In this scale for measuring pleasure he considered seven factors: intensity, endurance or duration, closeness in point of time, chance of being followed by sensations of the same kind, chance of being followed by sensations of the opposite kind, certainty or probability of happening, and the number of persons to which an act extends. The determination of right and wrong or choice of action is to be made by considering the factors related to each pleasure or pain and adding the total effect on all individuals to determine the balance. Only quantitative aspects of pleasure are considered and every one is to count for one and no one for more than one. Many people cannot readily evaluate or discern their own best interests or the best interests of society and therefore it is necessary for society to have "sanctions" which pile up the pains or increase the rewards to make the total consequences of an act more clearly evident. Thus the would-be thief can visualize the immediate gain received from stealing, but recognition of the potential pain which the "sanction" of jail will impose usually deters the unsocial conduct. Bentham classifies "sanctions" into four groups: political (e.g., legal penalties and rewards), physical (e.g., effects of gluttony), moral (e.g., public opinion) and religious (e.g., life hereafter).

John Stuart Mill (1806-1873) was a student of Bentham and

was groomed by Bentham and his father, James Mill, to carry on as a disciple of Bentham. Mill used the title *Utilitarianism* to refer to his pleasure theories and attempted to counter much of the criticism of Bentham's work by simplifying the "calculus" and introducing the concept that quality as well as quantity should be considered in evaluating pleasure. Mill reduced Bentham's seven factors to three: intensity, duration, and the number of persons to which an act extends. The factors of certainty and closeness in point of time relate to pleasures which have not yet come and there should be no need to measure that which does not exist. The factors related to chance of being followed by other sensations should merely be considered as a part of the total consequences of a pleasure. The quality of a pleasure can be judged by the number of wise and experienced people who prefer the pleasure and also by the accumulated experience of mankind. Pleasures or satisfactions must be related to the individual involved.

"Few human creatures would consent to be changed into any of the lower animals, for a promise of the fullest allowance of a beast's pleasures; no intelligent human being would consent to be a fool, no instructed person would be an ignoramus, no person of feeling and conscience would be selfish and base, even though they be persuaded that the fool, the dunce, or the rascal is better satisfied with his lot than they are with theirs. . . . A being of higher faculties requires more to make him happy. . . . It is indisputable that the being whose capacities of enjoyment are low, has the greatest chance of having them fully satisfied; and a highly endowed being will always feel that any happiness which he can look for, as the world is constituted, is imperfect. But he can learn to bear its imperfections, if they are at all bearable; and they will not make him envy the being who is indeed unconscious of the imperfections. . . . It is better to be a a human being dissatisfied than a pig satisfied; better to be Socrates dissatisfied than a fool satisfied. And if the fool, or the pig, are of different opinion, it is because they only know their own side of the question." (6:449)

Henry Sidgwick (1838-1900) is another proponent of utilitarianism who made some significant contributions to the theory.

The method of utilitarianism essentially involves a consideration of the probable consequences of two or more alternatives and a choice of the one which seems to give the greatest balance of pleasure. Sidgwick in his *Methods of Ethics* presents three important axioms which can give a more clear cut means for making a choice between several alternatives. These axioms are the *Maxim of Justice, Maxim of Prudence,* and the *Maxim of Benevolence.* The Maxim of Justice may be stated as whatever is right for one person is right for all similar persons in similar circumstances. The Maxim of Prudence indicates that a smaller present good is not to be preferred to a greater future good—all life should be considered and each part of life has equal worth with any future part. The Maxim of Benevolence indicates that each person is ethically bound to regard the good of any other individual as much as his own—one should not accept happiness for himself if it involves sacrificing a greater amount of happiness for some other human being.

2-6. THEORY OF FORMALISM. Some writers classify all ethical theories as either formalistic or teleological. Formalistic theories are concerned primarily with the motive for an act; an act is good, regardless of the consequences, if there was a proper motive or intent. Teleological theories judge an act by the end, goal, or consequence; only if these are good is the act good. For example, if one meant to give medicine, but through a mistake, the patient was poisoned and died, formalism would say the intent was good therefore the act was good; teleological theory would say the consequence was bad therefore the act was bad. However, even though each theory might classify the acts differently, undoubtedly reasoning proponents of either theory probably would have acted in a similar manner. It is only because the consequences could not be anticipated that they differ in terminology.

Probably the best known formalistic theory is that set forth by Immanuel Kant (1724-1804). Kant starts his *Fundamental Principles of the Metaphysics of Morals:*

"Nothing can possibly be conceived in the world, or even out of it, which can be called good . . . except a good will. Intelligence, wit, judgment, and the other *talents* of the mind, however they may be named, or courage, resolution, perseverance, as qualities of temperament, are undoubtedly good and desirable in many respects; but these gifts of nature may also be extremely bad and mischievous if the will which is to make use of them, and which therefore, constitutes what is called *character* is not good. . . . Power, riches, honor, even health, and the general well-being and contentment with one's condition which is called *happiness,* inspire pride, and often presumption, if there is not a good will to correct the influence of these on the mind, . . . thus a good will appears to constitute the indispensable condition of being worthy of happiness." (4:256)

Kant conceived only a single duty—that of developing a good will. The concept of formalism, of following duty, has also been applied in a pluralistic manner to such duties as following the laws of nature and laws of the land. Recent trends in plural formalism have seen rules and laws multiplied beyond all reason and imagination. Every conceivable type of force, both reward and punishment, is used to compel obedience to the rules. Rules are the instruments of bureaucracy and tyranny. Kant thought each man should be his own rule maker; and he need follow only *one* rule or moral law, the *categorical imperative.*

Kant expresses his categorical imperative: *"Act as if the maxim of thy action were to become by thy will a universal law of nature."* (4:268) The universal law thus involves a consideration of what would happen if everyone were to do as you propose to do. Right and wrong, if they are to have any meaning, must have the same meaning for everyone. It is as absurd to say that what is right for one person would under the same conditions be wrong for another as to expect the laws of gravity to apply to some but not to others. Wrongdoing is making an exception for oneself. Each person must obey the same rules he wants others to obey. The person who commits a wrong act adopts one course of action for himself but he wants others to follow a different one. Thus if all people were thieves, there would be no private property; and therefore it would be impossible to steal since stealing is the taking of another's property. The thief wants special privilege for himself only. Similarly in the case of the liar. If all men told lies there could be no real communication or trust of any man, thus leading to a break down of society. Kant does not even accept the "white" lie which is intended to avoid harm. The good will is formed by always acting right thus making right conduct a habit; and telling the occasional "white" lie breaks the habit of doing man's most important duty of developing the good will. One is not obligated to answer; but if an answer is given it should be the truth. One can never be sure of the ultimate consequences of a lie; and if there be unexpected disastrous consequences, the responsibility for the consequences must be borne by the one telling the "white" lie.

The categorical imperative indicates that it is one's duty to follow the course of action made evident when universalizing of the action demonstrates a social condition which is consistent and rational, regardless of the consequences to oneself. Kant strongly condemned any consideration of the consequences of an act, the focal point of right and wrong being the will to act consistently with reason; but one can also think of the universal law as being a most effective means of magnifying the consequences of an act so that the total consequences (e.g., pleasure or happiness) may be more readily evaluated. It may also be noted that Kant's Categorical Imperative and Sidgwick's Maxim of Justice are quite similar.

A principle which Kant indicates is implied in practical application of the categorical imperative is: "So act as to treat humanity, whether in thine own person or in that of any other, in every case as end withal, never as means only." (4:272) Thus it is always wrong to use people as merely a means to an end (e.g., to exploit others for personal gain, to put them in armies to die as a means of "defending" a geographical entity). Man is the most important of all ends for which we must strive—man must never be used, damaged or killed as a means to attain lesser or false ends. Kant's formalism does not tolerate the lack of deep convictions or the holding of false destructive ideas. It is not enough to do the "right" thing and follow the laws; the dictator operates by controlling ideas and having everyone "do the right thing" by following *his* laws. Belief should not be separated from action; and the man of good will does not justify any means to attain an end, either good or false. It is much too easy to justify or color the means to suit the situation. Thus an act when unjustified is "murder"; but the same act when justified becomes "euthanasia (mercy killing)" or "patriotism." Similarly, taking a man's property without his consent when unjustified is "stealing"; but when justified it becomes "commandeering."

2-7. SUMMARY. There are numerous variations, departures, extensions and combinations of the ethical theories briefly outlined in this chapter. The question usually arises: which of these many theories is best, which shall I attempt to follow? Too many people, particularly in social matters, feel they have to belong to and follow one particular doctrine. Just as there are multiple theories in ethics, politics, or economics, there are multiple methods which an engineer may use to solve a particular problem. For example, an engineer wishing to find the maximum deflection of a particular beam may do so by one or more of such methods as: double integration, moment-area, conjugate beam, virtual work or use of Castigliano's first theorem. The competent engineer welcomes having all these methods available to him. Each method may be more simple and/or accurate under specific instances. The engineer will usually have one or two methods which he prefers, and in which he has obtained the most experience; but he is always alert to choose the method which appears to be best for the particular problem at hand. He will also usually want to check his results by working the problem by at least two different methods. Ethical or social problems may be handled similarly. One need not follow blindly one doctrine. There may be personal preferences, but the proper choice of action can best be determined by applying several theories to the problem until a clearcut and consistent answer is evident.

Ethical theories are of little value unless there is considerable detailed discussion and examples. This appears evident in the principal theories which have influenced society. Within these ethical theories may be found major principles which are analogous to equations used in a method of engineering analysis. Every equation is based upon presuppositions and therefore there are limitations to its use; and one has only to read the pencraft of the critics of any particular ethical theory to become quite aware of these limitations. The ability to use ethical theories properly can only come about by properly directed continued application and experience. This does not necessarily mean that one should attempt to follow precisely an ethical theory such as Utilitarianism, for to do so one would have to carry around continually the writings of the founders and refer to these as though they were handbooks or cookbooks. What is important is that a systematic orderly way of thinking be developed—one which recognizes presuppositions and ultimate ends or purposes and continually adapts to conditions which are verified by observations. In the next chapter a systematic approach is presented in which ethical principles are used in the methodology of engineering (see Fig. 1-5) to solve ethical problems in a manner which is analogous to the use of equations in solving engineering problems.

ASSIGNMENTS

2.1 Make a list of the major principles included in the ethical theories presented in the chapter.

2.2 Make a list of other general ethical principles (e.g., the Golden Rule) of which you are aware.

2.3 Cite an example where each of the ethical principles listed above appears to lead to vague or uncertain conclusions.

BIBLIOGRAPHY

(1) ARISTOTLE. *Nichomachean Ethics*. Translated by W. D. Ross. (*Great Books of the Western World*, 9:339-436) Chicago: Encyclopaedia Britannica, Inc., 1952.

(2) AURELIUS, MARCUS. *Meditations*. Translated by George Long.

(Great Books of the Western World, 12:253-310) Chicago: Encyclopaedia Britannica, Inc., 1952.

(3) EPICTETUS. *Discourses.* Translated by George Long. *(Great Books of the Western World,* 12:105-245) Chicago: Encyclopaedia Britannica, Inc., 1952.

(4) KANT, IMMANUEL. *Fundamental Principles of the Metaphysics of Morals.* Translated by T. K. Abbott. *(Great Books of the Western World,* 42:253-87) Chicago: Encyclopaedia Britannica, Inc., 1952.

(5) MELDEN, A. I. *Essays in Moral Philosophy.* Seattle: University of Washington Press, 1958.

(6) MILL, JOHN STUART. *Utilitarianism.* *(Great Books of the Western World,* 43:445-76) Chicago: Encyclopaedia Britannica, Inc., 1952.

SUGGESTED ADDITIONAL READING

DRAKE, DURANT. *Problems of Conduct.* Boston: Houghton Mifflin Company, 1935. 520 pp.

HILL, THOMAS E. *Ethics in Theory and Practice.* New York: Thomas Y. Crowell Company, 1956. 429 pp.

MITCHELL, EDWIN T. *A System of Ethics.* New York: Charles Scribner's Sons, 1950. 559 pp.

PATTERSON, CHARLES H. *Moral Standards—An Introduction to Ethics.* New York: The Ronald Press Company, 1949. 514 pp.

PEPPER, STEPHEN C. *Ethics.* New York: Appleton-Century-Crofts, Inc., 1960. 351 pp.

ROGERS, REGINALD A. P. *A Short History of Ethics.* London: Macmillan and Co., 1945. 303 pp.

TSANOFF, RADOSLAV. *Ethics.* New York: Harper & Brothers, 1947. 385 pp.

CHAPTER 3

A Methodology of Ethics

3-1. APPROACHES TO ETHICAL BEHAVIOR.
Every person probably has at least some vague, superficial, unorganized ideas about the difference between right and wrong, the meaning of life, of happiness, of success, of beauty, and many other concepts involved in everyday affairs. We continuously receive these ideas from family and friends and from home, school, and religious institutions. The following are some commonly stated general approaches to ethical behavior and an evaluation of a few of the complex problems one faces in using each of these individual approaches:

Obey the laws of the land. The law is often indicated to be the minimum ethics which the particular society will accept. However, does the individual have the responsibility to judge the merit of the laws, or merely to obey? Our present legal system appears to be a confused mixture of acting as a threat to potential criminals, a device for removal from society, a ritual of expiation, and a prompter for moral reform. General attitudes of avoiding individual responsibility, of "let the government do it," have resulted in hundreds upon hundreds of legislators, at all levels of government, diligently and continuously writing thousands upon thousands of laws. The legislators in their anxiety to cover all actions and problems have often brought forth amateurish, excessive, inapplicable, and unenforceable laws. For example (2) laws have been passed which prohibit (*a*) walking through the streets with shoelaces undone, (*b*) wearing of suspenders, (*c*) biting one's landlord, (d) dogs from crying, (e) tickling a girl, (f) a woman from buying a new hat without her husband trying it on first, (g) riding on the roof of a taxicab, (h) a housewife from moving the furniture in her home without her husband's consent. Laws tend to emphasize the negative, pointing out what is considered wrong but rarely pointing out what is considered right. It is much easier to write new laws than it is to make the new law effective. It is fairly safe to say that few people obey all laws—particularly the many obsolete laws which have not been repealed. The mere passing of a law does not necessarily make people ethical. Even the lawyers, in their professional activities, have an extra-legal province of professional ethics. There are laws of right which are higher than the laws of the land. We must seek this higher standard to judge whether new laws are needed, whether a law is obsolete, whether a law is good, and to allow each individual deliberate reasoned choice of action.

Follow the recognized customs and ideals.   This may be considered a more comprehensive approach than merely following the laws, as one part of the customs of a society. However, customs and ideals, as well as laws, may not be rational in origin; often they are imposed by an individual or group in a position to dominate lives. Even if the custom and ideals were originally rational in origin, this approach implies that we must forever hold to them blindly or all is lost. Customs of the past have included cannibalism, incest, witch burning, and slavery. When a custom is in force, the path of least resistance is to conform; but can we afford to conform at the expense of truth, reason, and justice? We cannot be content to know what the customs and ideals are, and merely follow; but we must ask what they ought to be.

Follow the example of great men.   We may well follow the example of Christ, Buddha or Gandhi. However, many have followed the examples of Hitler and Mussolini. The major obstacles in this approach are the difficulty of knowing enough about any man's life to be able to have examples to follow for each of life's many problems and, most important, to have a standard by which to judge what man is truly great and deserves to be followed.

Follow the "Good Book" and religious authority.   Many people do not profess to follow any religion; many others are ignorant of and do not follow the religion to which they profess. When the "Good Book" is spoken of, some speak of the New Testament, others speak of the Old Testament, and still others speak of the Book of Mormon, the Koran, the Bhagavad-Gita, the Tao-Teh-king, or the Analects of Confucius. Does a Buddhist, or a member of any other of the hundreds of different religious sects, have good reason to follow the religion in which he was born and brought up, without fully considering all of the other religions? Assuming the particular "Good Book" and religion have been chosen wisely, can we be sure that the religious authorities are interpreting the ideals correctly? Religious authorities have built great organizations to aid in extending ideals; but too often the ideals have been forgotten and attention centered in the organization. Yet someone must interpret the will of God, at least about such modern innovations as television, nuclear energy, and space travel which do not appear to be mentioned as such in the "Good Books." Historically, it can be seen that the will of God has been interpreted to justify such actions as animal and human sacrifice, burning at the stake and massacres of the unbelievers. Most people would justify promoting the Commandment "Thou shalt not kill" by taking the weapon of a potential murderer, without his knowledge, and thus breaking the Commandment "Thou shalt not steal." Similarly, even the very devout would justify working on the Sabbath if otherwise the safety of an entire community would be in jeopardy. The faithful practice of a religion is a very complex and difficult task. There are probably no ethical situations which are exactly the same as those found in religious precedent. Apparently some other outside means or standard is needed to know if religious ideals are being interpreted and applied correctly, and upon occasion to justify breaking of the ideal.

Strive for the welfare of society.   No man can live adequately alone. Men are largely affected by circumstances and therefore many have made one of their great aims in life the improvement of man's external conditions—his society. Indeed, down through history there have been numerous individuals and nations who considered themselves the ones most capable of leading other individuals and nations in the direction of the ideal society—and those who disagreed were put to the sword. Do we want the regimentation of the totalitarian state which may decide that individuals must be sacrificed for the good of the state—and how does one know what is good for the state? It is too easy for the state to do something wrong if it doesn't have to take the time to make the one who is sacrificing, believe and want to do so voluntarily. Society and the state is possible only by some subordination of the individual, and the individual ordinarily gains more than he loses by subordination; but the subordination should be voluntary, for the state exists for the individual, not the individual for the state. If the individual must yield before force, the decision has no ethical value for him. If we strive for the welfare of a state which leaves men free to reason and to act, a state which places in the most honorable and commanding position the intellectually and ethically elite, again we must first accomplish a most complex and difficult outside task to establish and interpret the ideals upon which it must be founded. The Communist society expresses the ideal: "From everyone according to his abilities, and to everyone according to his needs"; but how is one to determine who "needs" an automobile or a television set when there are not enough for all? Desiring to strive for the welfare of society, but not knowing what kind of a society one should strive for, is like desiring to aid the sick but through ignorance giving poison instead of medicine.

Follow one's conscience.   What we consider right or wrong is largely dependent upon what one is used to, becoming in essence conditioned reflexes which may be called the conscience. The conscience may be a prior judgment of right and wrong, an anticipation of the opinions of others, or fear of punishment. It develops from prior experiences with the laws, customs, ideals, religion, and the total of society and environment. As each new situation is at least slightly different from those prior, it is relatively easy to rationalize away the conscience. It could be said that the conscience causes a man to follow, as a man follows the automobile he drives. The conscience tends to be primarily negative in telling what is wrong, but not what is right. We hear and speak of people who have no conscience; but, more correctly, it should be said that their conscience is different. It is to be expected that if the past environment is different and wrong, then the conscience may develop to be different and wrong. Thus, each man needs some outside standard by means of which he can check the fallibility of his conscience.

Follow reason and logic.   It has been said that if one wishes to be the monarch of a little world, command thyself through reason; but all too few can reason well—or wish to reason. Too many men reason primarily about what they have done, instead of what they should do. Much of each man's world is there by precedent, and it is difficult to reason him out of something he was never reasoned into. Reason and the logic of the syllogism are closely allied. A syllogism may have a major premise, a minor premise and a conclusion, respectively: All ducks have web feet; Donald is a duck; therefore, Donald has web feet. However, Donald may have no feet—a "logical" conclusion has been obtained, but it is based upon the incorrect major premise that all ducks have web feet. Thus reason cannot stand by itself—there must at least be truths to reason with. Also mere reason cannot determine its own insufficiency, the difference between right and wrong reasoning; nor can it judge the quality of reasoning, for some reasoning must be better than others. One can no more follow reason alone, than the eye alone seeing something exists can judge whether or not it should exist.

Strive for happiness.   Striving for happiness is an essential element of Utilitarian theory, a well-known and popularly applied theory. Unfortunately, of all the millions who are frenziedly seeking happiness, all too few know just what they are seeking. Some think of happiness as being wealth, power, fame, or sensual pleasure. Wealth can be a burden that only death unloads; it can create more wants than it satisfies, for the universe does not have sufficient resources to satisfy all the desires that only one person may possibly have. When one achieves power, there still may be unanswered: what is to be done with the power, to achieve happiness? To achieve and maintain fame one may have to conform continuously to a fickle changing opinion of the public—is this happiness? The satisfaction of sensual pleasures often is followed by extreme melancholy, giving temporary gratification but not necessarily happiness. There are many examples of individuals who have sought and found wealth, power, fame, and sensual pleasure, but who do not appear to have found happiness. Some questions that may be asked about happiness are: is it a necessary reciprocal, that is, does one have to give it to receive it? Do we wish to be happy, or just happier than others? Can happiness be achieved by adjusting to being without it? How do we measure the quality of happiness? These questions, and many more, must be answered before one is prepared to strive for happiness; and these questions cannot be answered by the mere striving. Again, some outside standard and/or means are needed.

3-2. THE METHODOLOGY OF ENGINEERING APPLIED TO ETHICS.   In the previous section there was an attempt to show why each of the indicated individual approaches to ethical behavior are insufficient by themselves. Using only an approach such as "striving for happiness" in trying to solve an ethical problem is analogous to trying to solve an engineering problem by using only an equation without knowing any facts, purposes, causes, etc. Knowing additional applicable equations or principles can be helpful in obtaining and checking a solution; but a solution cannot be obtained, no matter how many equations are available, unless all the necessary constituent parts (e.g., fact, purposes) are available for use in the total methodology of engineering (See Fig. 1-5). Similarly, using all the approaches (e.g., following customs, religious ideals, conscience) can be most helpful in obtaining and checking a solution; but these approaches are only a part of a total methodology of ethics needed to obtain a solution to a problem which might be acceptable and communicable to others. The solution to an ethical problem must be acceptable and communicable to people having different customs, religions, conscience, etc., a condition of differences which exists even within a neighborhood within a single city.

The remarkable success of the engineering methodology in solving so many of the material problems of the world lies largely in the cooperative development of two major constituents of the methodology: definitions and assumptions. Ordinary dictionaries are inadequate in defining the complex concepts that the engineer needs in his daily work. In order to fill this need, engineers, working with scientists and mathematicians, have developed their own vocabulary and definitions which usually can be used efficiently to communicate with other engineers throughout the world. Ordinary dictionaries are similarly inadequate in defining basic complex ethical concepts such as happiness, good, evil, truth, etc.; and, unfortunately, there appears to be no available integrated set of definitions which might allow reasonable efficiency in communication in the area of ethics.

The extent of the cooperative effort of the engineering profession in establishing basic assumptions is probably not as readily evident to most engineers, as is the work done in establishing definitions. Examples of some cooperatively developed assumptions used in everyday engineering work are: the design life of an automobile, the factor of safety to be used and the design load on a structure. These assumptions are not developed by mathematics or equations, but usually only after elaborately considered and compromised value judgments. Thus, one may look up in an engineering code or handbook, that a recommended (assumed) safe live load is 40 pounds per square foot for a building. This does not mean that the actual live load will be 40 pounds per square foot, nor that the average or maximum load will be 40 pounds per square foot; for it is quite possible that an occupant of the building, who is completely ignorant of such things as design loads, may install equipment having a weight far exceeding the design loads. The recommended live loads represents an estimate of probable maximum loads introduced by (it is hoped) intelligent users of the facility. This also involves the recognition that there may possibly be unintelligent occupants, but if costs are to be kept within some (assumed) reasonable range, this risk must be incurred. An engineer might very justifiably argue: "I believe human life cannot be measured in dollars. I believe that we should therefore reduce the risk of collapse to an insignificant point; and I recommend that we should all assume design loads of 5000 pounds per square foot." Obviously if one engineer assumes 40 and another 5000 pounds per square foot they could never come anywhere close to agreement on the solution to the problem of designing the building.

Two engineers can agree on the solution to a typical engineering problem only if they start out with the same purposes, causes, assumptions, definitions, facts, applicable principles, and idealizations and use these in an organized methodology, without making careless mistakes. It might therefore be anticipated that an agreement on the solution to an ethical problem would be unlikely unless the parties start out with the same purposes, causes, assumptions, definitions, facts, applicable principles, and idealizations and use them in an organized methodology, without making careless mistakes.

A common reaction to the idea of solving ethical problems by an engineering methodology involves the comment that human beings are inconsistent, unpredictable, and variable; and therefore the "precise" methods used by the engineer are not applicable. Yet, the inability to predict precisely the effect of lightning striking a plane in flight, a tornado hitting a building, or an automobile crashing into a telephone pole does not prevent engineers from designing planes, buildings and automobiles. Under certain conditions an engineer can take an inconsistent, unpredictable, and variable material, such as iron ore, and by a process of refinement he can obtain steel rods which have some characteristics that are quite well predictable, statistically. Similarly, under certain conditions, the actions of human beings are quite predictable: as in the case of a military drill team or in the response of a thirsty man to the offer of a drink of water.

No engineer ever obtains the "right" or "best possible" answer to a practical engineering problem. He may obtain the "right" answer based upon the assumptions made; but it can be quite certain that the assumptions made are not the "best possible." Thus, if he were to assume the "best possible" durability for his design, it would have to be designed to last for eternity and no one could afford it, even if he were capable of designing something for eternity. If he were to assume the "best possible" cost as the criterion for design, he would probably have to design something which would function at minimum efficiency and last only an infinitesimal period of time. If he were to assume the "best possible" efficiency of operations as the design criterion, he would have to know all the advances in technology forthcoming in the future, i.e., he would need to have infinite knowledge.

The truly great contribution of the engineering profession (and its methodology) to society is its willingness and ability, in spite of much ignorance about the materials and forces of nature, to perform needed services within a time limit and with whatever financial resources are available. It is to be expected that if an engineer had more time and more money available, he could turn out a better design; and with infinite time and infinite money he might be able to turn out the "best possible" design. The "good" engineer learns to compromise his assumptions with respect to such factors as need, cost, durability, efficiency, time, and safety. When two "good" engineers agree on their assumptions and other aspects of the total methodology, then they may agree on an approximation of the "right" answer.

In solving ethical problems to find the "right" answer (what ought to be done) it should be recognized that the "ought" is also necessarily dependent upon the basic assumptions used. Nor is the "right" answer the "best possible" answer, for this would require infinite wisdom. The "right" answer to an ethical problem, just as in the case of an engineering problem, is that which is "best" in the light of our meager knowledge and abilities to function as reasoning beings in judging consistency with assumption and observation. This means that we must continuously be alert to evaluate and check our knowledge of the facts and the reasoning used to interpret, modify and improve our "best possible" answers.

Figure 3-1 shows a proposed methodology of ethics, which is a slight modification of the methodology of engineering used in analysis, design, and production (Fig. 1-5). The only change involves an addition, in the realm of abstraction, of assumed

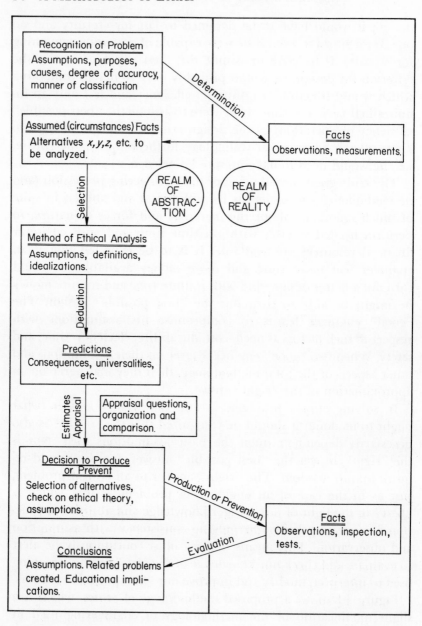

Fig. 3-1 Methodology of Ethics

(circumstances) facts or alternative courses of actions which are to be analyzed in the search for what one "ought" to do. These assumed facts are then combined with the facts obtained in the realm of reality and used in essentially the same methodology of engineering. Available methods of analysis (principles, equations) for ethical deductions have been discussed earlier in this text, with the Universal Law (Kants' categorical imperative) and the Utilitarian Principle probably being amongst the simplest to apply. An integrated set of basic definitions and assumptions, as vital constituent parts of the methodolgy of ethics, are presented in the next two sections of this chapter. Many more definitions and assumptions are needed for efficient use of the methodology; and undoubtedly those presented herewith can be improved upon. It is hoped that those presented may serve as a foundation for further additions and improvements to be made by each reader. Sections 3-5 through 3-8 of this chapter present background discussion and information which should aid in the proper application of the methodology. Examples of the application of the methodology of ethics are presented in § 3-9.

3-3. DEFINITIONS. There can be no logical discourse amongst men when there are no definitions, or there are wrong definitions, or disagreement in definitions. By definition we refer to a statement of the meaning or meanings of a word. The same word can have a number of different meanings in ordinary usage. For example, the word "light" could be used in the following ways, with respective meanings shown in parentheses:

"It is best to travel light"	(unburdened)
"Turn on the overhead light"	(illumination)
"This puts a new light on the matter"	(interpretation)
"The plane is going to light"	(land)
"May I borrow a light"	(fire)
"The light is broken"	(window pane)
"She has a light complexion"	(fair)
"It is three light-years away"	(distance)
"Eat a light meal"	(digestible and small)
"He walked about in a light mood"	(gay)
"He made light of the situation"	(trivial)

Most of the important intangible words, such as truth, good, pleasure, etc., which are basic to ethical discourse are each also ordinarily used (and abused) in many different ways. A number of these basic definitions particularly deserving of study and consideration for further use are presented at the end of this section. Additional definitions, of lesser importance, are included in Appendix B. Many of these definitions are adaptations from the *Ethics* of Benedict De Spinoza, who probably has done the most comprehensive work of presenting a studied, integrated set of definitions of these intangibles.

These definitions may generally be classified as stipulative Aristotelian definitions. They are stipulative in that often the meanings are not those of ordinary usage, but are given a meaning which appears best for application to ethical discourse. The Aristotelian definition attempts to include both the encompassing class or group and the characteristics or properties which distinguish from others within the given class (e.g., "mother" defined as a "female parent"—"parent" is the encompassing class, and "female" is the characteristic which distinguishes from the other parent). In stating and applying definitions, one should be alert to avoid inadequacies such as the following:

a) Circularity—using the word (or derivative of, or a synonym) being defined in the definition (e.g., "patriotism is a feeling shown by a patriot").

b) Negativity—defining something as being the negative of something else, which also has not been defined; or stating it is not something (e.g., "an automobile is not a tree") yet leaving a host of possible things which it is.

c) Obscurity—ambiguous, metaphorical, or unintelligible definitions (e.g., "love is a baring of the soul"; or "love is a difficult complex maintenance of individual integrity throughout the incalculable processes of inter-human polarity.").

d) Incongruity—using definitions which are either too broad or too narrow to distinguish the word being defined (e.g., defining a "pencil" as "a writing instrument" is too broad as the definition also includes pens; defining a "pencil" as "a writing instrument made out of wood and lead" is too narrow as it excludes automatic pencils made out of other materials.

e) Extraneousness—stating unique complex attributes or properties that do not give the essentials needed for a clear understanding of the word being defined (e.g., "a circle is a figure having an area equal to pi times the square of the radius"; such a definition is unlikely to aid one in recognizing a circle).

Basic Definitions for Use in Ethical Discourse*

CONSCIENCE—*acquired knowledge that certain acts are approved and rewarded, while other acts are disapproved and punished.*

CONSEQUENCE—*the effects of a specific course of action which can be appraised and evaluated by contemporary reason.*

COURAGE—*the desire to do something good, which others, who are equal, fear to attempt.* Courage does not involve merely the taking of risks. A man who drinks polluted water, without knowing it, is taking a risk but is not performing what we would call a courageous act. Courage involves a knowledge of the risk, a risk not hidden by ignorance or emotional excitement, and a calm appraisal that the worthiness of the cause justifies the risk.

EDUCATION—*a process of developing the rational faculties (reason).* The mere acquisition of knowledge of facts, such as names, dates, and opinions, is not necessarily education. The acquisition of facts should be the base upon which rests the primary activity of developing good attitudes, insight, and judgment. See also *Reason* and *Training.*

ESCAPE—*gratification or pleasure obtained by temporary avoidance or ignoring of the proximate cause of suffering or pain.* (e.g., gratification may be obtained by dulling the senses to pain by means of drunkenness, but the proximate cause of pain remains; pleasure may be obtained from escape (possibly a walk in the woods) if one comes back refreshed and inspired with new ability to remove the proximate cause of pain). See also *Pleasure* and *Gratification.*

ETHICS—*the science of determining values in human conduct (what ought to be done).*

* See Appendix B for supplementary definitions.

FACT—See *Truth*.

FREEDOM—*a state in which all endeavors are led by reason.* A mere lack of restraint or restrictions against fulfilling a desire is not freedom, for we are not free of the causes of the desire nor may we have the ability to fulfill our desires (e.g., one may desire and be "free" to spend a million dollars, but not have a million dollars; or desire and be "free" to run a mile in two minutes, but have no legs). The Ontological argument between free-will or self-determination and fatalism is not considered pertinent.

GOOD—*that which, in accordance with reason, contributes to existence and/or aids in the accomplishment of man's purpose.* See also *Reason.*

GRATIFICATION—*an interpretation of the attainment of (immediate) pleasure, determined solely by application of the physical senses.* See also *Pleasure.*

HAPPINESS—*a state in which good is being accomplished.*

INTELLECTUALISM—*the endeavor to achieve good beyond that of satisfying self-interest.* Self-interest may be satisfied by wealth, sensual pleasure, or fame. Intellectualism goes beyond the self, seeking friendship, knowledge, the best social structure, etc.

JUDGMENT—*an endeavor to determine the extent of good or truth in a specific set of circumstances.*

JUSTICE—*an endeavor in the direction of the greatest good for a specific set of circumstances.* This definition does not involve in any way the concept of equality, for equality is usually impossible in typical instances of the application of justice. Certainly the life of the condemned murderer is not necessarily equal in value to the life of the man he killed; nor is it likely that a year in prison can be equated in value to the losses incurred by the crime committed. Our common law principle of Caveat Emptor (let the buyer beware) clearly illustrates the fact that our courts cannot reasonably attempt to measure the exact equality of an exchange of goods or services for money.

KNOWLEDGE—*the summation of acquired correlated truths.*

NEED—*that which barely sustains existence.* Too many men are overly absorbed with attempting to satisfy all their self-desires, placing them in the guise of needs. It is unlikely that the universe has the resources or the individual the time to satisfy all desires. See also *Intellectualism.*

PAIN—*a decrease, as evaluated by reason, in the power to act towards good.* See also *Pleasure* and *Suffering.*

PLEASURE—*an increase, as evaluated by reason, in the power to act towards good.* Based only upon the use of the physical senses one might receive gratification (see *Gratification*) from food which has in it a tasteless deadly poison; but in accordance with reason, the sensation must be defined as pain. Conversely, the sensation received while a dentist is drilling a tooth to remove decay may appear to be suffering (see *Suffering*); but in accordance with reason, the sensation must be defined as pleasure. The writer has heard statements to the effect: "I sure had a good time (pleasure) last night—I was so drunk I don't remember what happened; but I sure had a good time last night." The mere statement by the individual that he had pleasure does not necessarily make it so, for the physical senses are most fallible. Our physical senses indicate, for example, that the sun travels around the earth, that the moon changes its shape and that the telephone pole in the distance is much shorter than the pole nearby—these perceptions are corrected by reason. There are an infinite variety of activities a man may choose from, each of which may give pleasures of varying quantity and type. Pleasures may be typed as appetitive, intellectual, or escape. Appetitive pleasures (e.g., eating, sex) have characteristics of being temporary in nature and having diminishing returns (as the amount of activity increases the amount of pleasure received decreases). The intellectual pleasures (e.g., friendship, knowledge) have characteristics of greater permanency and increasing returns (as the amount of activity increases the amount of pleasure increases). Escape (see definition of) may sometimes result in pleasure and sometimes merely in gratification. Reason will determine the proper balance between types of pleasure, without the usual undue emphasis on pleasures of the appetite and escape.

REALITY—*that which is, was, or will be.* See also *Truth.*

REASON—*a process of evaluation using orderly, systematic thinking, aided by the best available instruments for physical measurements, computing devices, and the best judgment of others.*

SUCCESS—*achievement of progressive good.* Success is defined, in more ordinary usage, as the obtaining of what one desires or intends. Many people bring about considerable unhappiness by having un-

attainable goals or desires and then, upon the basis of the latter definition, consider themselves complete failures. A healthier outlook is to
consider any progress as success, and to consider the individual who
makes the most and fastest progress as the most successful.

SUFFERING—*an interpretation of the recipience of pain, determined
solely by application of the physical senses.* See also *Pain* and *Pleasure.*

TRAINING—*a process of developing the ability to perform a task in
a specific manner.* See also *Education.*

TRUTH (FACT)—*a statement, proposition or belief having the best
(in accordance with contemporary reason) correspondence with a
specific reality.* All truths can only be approximations of reality (e.g.,
we would have to measure a length with infinite accuracy in order to
be able to state its real length); and we should recognize that many
truths of today will, as knowledge and judgment increases, have to be
discarded in the future as being either too inaccurate or incorrect.
See also *Reality* and *Reason.*

3-4. ASSUMPTIONS.   In Chapter 1 it was pointed out
that the orderly, systematic thinker should be aware of his assumptions—assumptions are the foundation of all theories and their applications. The writer, working together with others, has found the
following basic assumptions to be reasonably acceptable and to
serve rather effectively as the foundation for discourse and problem
solving in the area of ethics (these are based upon society as it
ought to be, not is):

(1) **Man and the universe exist and will continue to exist.**   This
assumes that there is a reality, and all is not, for example, a figment
of man's imagination; also, that this reality will continue to exist
for the foreseeable future although there may be evolutionary
changes occurring.

(2) **Each man should expect to live for the average statistical
life-span, and each period of this anticipated life has equal value.**
This assumes that the future, although indefinite and uncertain,
should not be sacrificed for the present which is only one moment
in the total span.

(3) **Every man has a purpose (beyond mere existence), and every
man must be given equal opportunity to fulfill this purpose.**

Most parts and objects we observe appear to have a "purpose" beyond mere existence. For example, the eye has a "purpose" of seeing, the ear, of hearing, and the red blood corpuscles exist or live and die (generally independently of the total body) with a primary purpose of transmitting oxygen. Man designs a table or a chair, and causes them to exist in this form, for a purpose. In designing a building we must first decide whether its purpose is to be a warehouse, a hospital, etc. It should therefore follow that each man was designed for a purpose, and each man should "know" (assume) the design purpose of his life. A corollary of the latter part of the above assumption is that *every man has some worth alive—no man is to be intentionally destroyed.* One often hears arguments that we should encourage evolutionary preservation of the strong and destruction of the weak. "Why not kill off (or use for medical experimentation) the incurably ill, the feeble, the insane, the immoral and use the natural resources thereby saved to aid others?" If such ideas were carried to their extremes and society did not protect the weak and feeble, the human race would be destroyed, for who are the weakest and most feeble but the babies? Who would decide who was to be destroyed? Private revenge and crime could creep into the decision making. Cures for the "uncurable" may be brought forth any day. If the purpose of the eye is to see, we do not expect any one eye to see everything there is to see, nor all eyes to see the same things, nor all eyes to see equally well; nor should we condemn any man for similar failings. The man with one arm may teach us all how to make more effective use of each of the arms we have. It should be our obligation to encourage and protect the individuality of each man in his attempt to fulfill his purpose.

(5) **Each man's purpose is to seek, to correlate, and to disseminate truths, and to strive to aid and improve the existence of other men.** Of course each man must strive for and be able to maintain his own existence (and satisfy the necessary appetites of existence) before he can fulfill the purpose of this existence. Too many men find the struggle for survival (existence) so severe, that they have little or no time to consider the purpose of their

existence; many other men have the time, but do not use it for more than merely existing. One might seek this purpose, which is beyond mere existence, by considering what one would want to do with his life if he was entirely relieved of the necessity to struggle to survive; that is, if one had "the gift of existence" (all the material things one needs to exist, including even luxuries, merely for the asking) what would you do with your time? Or one might look back through the history of mankind and attempt to see what respected men have done beyond merely existing. It appears evident such activities that might be noted including exploration, scientific discovery, art, literature, and great services to mankind are encompassed by assumption No. 5.

Some might contend that the only purpose of our existence is to prepare for a life hereafter; however, in most instances, the means of preparing for the life hereafter would be the same as the given purpose (assumption No. 5) for existence. Others, upon the basis of similar questioning and observations, might contend that the purpose of existence is to seek power, or to seek happiness. Here again it is a matter of which is assumed first, for it might be asked what does one want the power to do or how does one seek happiness? It is believed that if one has the power to maintain satisfactorily his existence and to strive towards fulfilling his purpose, he will be finding happiness.

(6) No man, nor the human race, can know all of reality (all truths) and therefore, should be most concerned with those truths which have the greatest generality, particularly those involving the individual and social existence of man. This assumption indicates that if we wish to seek, to correlate, and to disseminate truths and recognize that there is not enough time in a lifetime to seek all truths, we ought first to attempt to decide (assume) whether or not all truths have equal value; and if not, determine means of discrimination. Ordinarily, we would be less concerned with determining random, uncorrelated truths, such as counting the number of blades of grass in a specific square foot of the front lawn or counting the number of grains of sand in a cubic foot of earth underneath the grass, then we would be in determining the general characteristics of all blades of grass or all grains of sand. The correlation between several truths is also more important than the finding of an isolated truth.

(7) **Life, property, and freedom are inalienable rights of every man.** This assumption indicates that the ideal state shall not have the right to take a man's life under any circumstances, his property without due compensation, or prevent his action when it is demonstrated that he acts with reason. To do otherwise is to invite the totalitarian state where no one can be sure that he is not expendable for the "good" of the state. A corollary of this assumption is that the state exists for the benefit of man, not man for the benefit of the state.

(8) **We should seek to use the least amount of material, energy, and time to fulfill a purpose.** This conforms to natural "laws of conservation of energy."

(9) **When a problem does not involve appraisal of major or radical changes in the existing social order, it shall be assumed that the existing social order is to be maintained, with allowances for gradual evolutionary changes.** Most ethical problems must be solved within the framework of an existing social order; and these problems are not likely to have any major immediate effect on the social order.

Ethical discourse between individuals having elements of a common background can also be facilitated by making additional assumptions of truths which may not be readily acceptable to an individual coming from a different social order. Thus two citizens of the U. S. A. might readily accept a modified capitalism and monogamy as vital elements to achieve the best social structure. These assumptions, however, would probably not be acceptable to a Communist from a Mohammedan country.

3-5. ENDS AND MEANS. In ordinary usage an *end* is considered to be something we aim at or choose for its own sake; whereas *means* are considered to be things chosen because of the results yielded. Thus, if one walks for health, walking would be considered the means to achieve the end of health.

A commonly heard statement is "the end justifies the means." That is, we can justify any means of accomplishing something, if the end accomplished is considered to be good. Common usage also frequently colors the same means upon the basis of the end achieved, or its justification. Thus, when the means are unjustified it is "murder;" when the means are justified it becomes "capital punishment," or "military art." The fallacy in "the end justifies the means" should become evident if further analysis is made of these so-called ends and means.

Following a sequence of ends and means: one may attend college as a means of earning a degree, as an end. But why does one want a degree? The degree might be considered to be a means of earning a living, as an end. But why does one want to earn a living? Earning a living may be considered a means of continuing to exist, as an end. But why does one want to continue to exist? Other sequences of ends and means could also invariably be led back to this same latter question; that is, it will be found that all of our so-called ends are themselves only means to an ultimate (assumed) end or purpose such as that stated in § 3-4, assumption 5. We may effectively set for ourselves what may be considered intermediate ends, such as earning a degree or becoming registered as a professional engineer; but it should be recognized that these are only means to achieve an ultimate end or purpose of existence.

In actuality, therefore, means and (intermediate) ends cannot be separated, for the intermediate ends are themselves only means to an ultimate end. In evaluating any action the total effect of both means and (intermediate) ends must be considered in determining the good—just as we might evaluate the worthwhileness of an intermediate end of spending an afternoon at the beach by considering the total effect, including the means, which may involve a hazardous and wearying drive to and from the beach.

It should therefore be evident that the "end" cannot justify the means, that evil means must never be used under any circumstances. Both the means and intermediate end have an effect upon achieving one's ultimate purpose; and the means can have more effect than the intermediate end. All too often there may be neglect of the effect of the means in weakening the will and character of the individual, or in debasing the social environment; thus setting up a pattern which later results in attitudes and desire for revenge, cruelty, and ill-will. All is not necessarily well that "ends" well.

3-6. THE POSITIVE APPROACH. In many problems and concepts of science and engineering there are considered to be in existence only the positive quantities involved. For example, there is an absolute zero of temperature and only positive quantities of heat exist although we commonly use both the word "heat" and its antonym "cold". Cold does not exist in reality, but is indicative only of relative amounts of the positive quantity, heat. In ethical discourse there are many advantages to taking a similar positive approach. Thus, in considering people one may say there is no such thing as an ugly person, only some less beautiful than others. In evaluating character one can find some good in every person, and a much healthier atmosphere is created if effort is concentrated on seeking this good.

The Golden Rule, or similar statement, is found in many cultures and is usually stated positively to the effect: "Do unto others as you would have them do unto you." In some cultures, particularly in the Orient, statements similar to the Golden Rule are found expressed in the negative to the effect: "Do not do unto others what you would not have them do unto yourself." At first glance it may appear that the positive or negative statements would serve eqaully well. However, if the negative statement were to be followed to the extreme it might be interpreted to be best that one should not do *anything;* and in order not to do anything the ideal state of existence might be one of permanent stupefaction under an opiate.

Many people consider justice done if "an eye for an eye, a tooth for a tooth," considered in the negative, is applied. Thus, if a man takes a life, it is considered just if society takes the murderer's life. Yet, would there not be more justice if the positive approach was used and when a man takes a life society attempt, inasmuch as possible, to have the murderer replace a life? Society thus would impose on the murderer the tasks of two men: the obligation to support himself and (by possibly working a total of 80 hours a week, instead of 40) the obligation to aid the dependents of the murdered man.

It is easier to offer negative criticism than positive suggestions; but the positive suggestions are much more likely to result in the desired change. Life can be better fulfilled with positive opinions and positive actions.

3-7. PRINCIPLES AND RULES. *Principles* such as Kant's Categorical Imperative or the Utilitarian Principle should be followed or applied to all actions, if an individual wishes to be consistently ethical. However, ethical *rules* only need be generally followed, with exceptions to be made when adequately justified. Ethical rules can give us ready, tried precepts of reason which may be memorized or quickly looked up to help insure the correct action. Ethical rules may be placed in three classifications:

(1) Fundamental rules—rules which apply to all people (e.g., "do not break a promise")

(2) Local rules—rules which apply only to certain groups (e.g , codes of ethics applying to the practice of engineering, medicine, or law)

(3) Neutral rules—rules which could apply equally well if the opposite was chosen (e.g., "drive on the right side of the road"); but some choice must be made so that people may expect and rely on conformity.

Ethical rules are established, justified, modified (and occasionally may be broken) by application of ethical principles. One should know the intent or purpose behind a rule and how it fits into a system of rules, for proper application. The complicated nature of human affairs prevents ethical rules being framed which require no exceptions. Certainly a promise to take a child to the circus should be broken if the child develops a 105° temperature, yet still desires to go to the circus. Ethical rules can differ, even be opposite, in different geographical or social conditions, yet both may be justified by the same principle. Ethical rules intended for ordinary men should not be too far beyond the capacities of ordinary men in ordinary occasions or there may be a general breakdown in compliance (e.g., prohibition), thus adversely affecting compliance with other rules. On the other hand, rules which will generally receive compliance only from saints or heros (e.g., "turn the other cheek") can set an example or goal for ordinary men; and other rules may be changed in this direction as the level of ethics of the ordinary man rises.

3-8. ETHICAL PRACTICES OF THE PROFES-SION. Probably the most ancient and well known written statement of professional ethics is the *Hippocratic Oath* of the medical profession. Suggestions related to the *Oath* date back to Egyptian papyri of 2000 B.C. The Greek medical writings making up the *Hippocratic Collection* were put together about 400 B.C. The present form of the Hippocratic Oath originated about 300 A.D. Most of the major professional organizations in the United States were founded during a relatively short period in the latter half of the nineteenth century; and most of them adopted the present form of their codes of ethics during a relatively short period at the beginning of the twentieth century. The American Medical Association, founded in 1847, adopted its *Principles of Medical Ethics* in 1912. The American Society of Civil Engineers, founded in 1852, adopted its *Code of Ethics* in 1914. The American Society of Mechanical Engineers, founded in 1880, adopted its *Code of Ethics* in 1914. The Institute of Electrical and Electronic Engineers (originally the American Institute of Electrical Engineers), founded in 1884, adopted its *Code of Principles of Professional Conduct* in 1912. The American Institute of Architects, founded in 1857, adopted its *Principles of Professional Practice and The Canons of Ethics* in 1909. The American Bar Association, founded in 1878, adopted its *Canons of Professional Ethics* in 1908.

The adoption of the comprehensive *Principles of Medical Ethics* appears to have followed closely behind the efforts in 1910 of the American Medical Association to establish standards and classifications for medical schools. Whereas laws to regulate the practice of medicine were established as early as 1639, most of the other professions were not regulated to any appreciable extent until the early part of the 20th century. After the Civil War there was a greatly increased feeling that it was undemocratic and un-American to grant special privilege to the professions, particularly the legal profession. A number of states passed statutes upholding the right of every voter of good moral character to practice law. This attitude appears to have resulted in a rising tide of irresponsibility and commercialism; and a consequent reaction to establish standards of character, education and experience started at the turn of the twentieth century. These standards were promoted as states, one after the other, began to pass registration laws (see § 4-5) controlling the practices of engineering, architecture, law, and the other professions, and the various national professional organizations adopted their codes of ethics.

Professional activities cannot be based upon the major common law premise used in ordinary business relations *caveat emptor,* "let the buyer beware." A written code of ethics declares before all the world the high standards which are professed and gives an understanding of what the public may expect in their relations with members of the profession. The code also is a helpful guide to the members of the profession in informing them what is expected of each member and what they may expect of each other. The public has come to expect competence, trustworthiness, and expeditious action; and the unethical actions of a few can arouse public indignation which may condemn and punish a profession at large through excessive legislation or boycott. The promotion of and adherence to ethical ideals brings the mutual gain of building respect for oneself by building respect for the profession.

A code of ethics is a set of local rules (see § 3-7) which represents the sum total *evaluation* (not merely appraisal—see Fig. 3-1) by a group of individuals of wide experience, of past practices and problems which are commonly encountered in the profession. *The Canons of Ethics for Engineers,* published in 1947 by the Engineer's Council for Professional Development, have been adopted by most engineering societies and are used as standards of ethical practices by a number of state registration boards.

However, many of the engineering societies have also retained their own codes of ethics, primarily because of problems believed unique to that branch of engineering. The National Society of Professional Engineers, in 1957, developed supplementary statements, which are called "Rules of Professional Conduct," as an aid in understanding the *Canons of Ethics*. The E C.P.D. *Canons of Ethics*, the "Rules of Professional Conduct," and the *Engineers' Creed*, adopted by N.S.P.E. in 1954, are reprinted below, by permission:

ENGINEERS' CREED

As a Professional Engineer, I dedicate my professional knowledge and skill to the advancement and betterment of human welfare.

I pledge:

    To give the utmost of performance;

    To participate in none but honest enterprise;

    To live and work according to the laws of man and the highest standards of professional conduct;

    To place service before profit, the honor and standing of the profession before personal advantage, and the public welfare above all other considerations.

In humility and with need for Divine Guidance, I make this pledge.

ADOPTED BY
NATIONAL SOCIETY OF PROFESSIONAL ENGINEERS
JUNE, 1954

CANONS OF ETHICS FOR ENGINEERS

AND

RULES OF PROFESSIONAL CONDUCT

Foreword

Honesty, justice and courtesy form a moral philosophy which, associated with mutual interest among men, constitutes the foundation of ethics. The engineer should recognize such a standard, not in passive observance, but as a set of dynamic principles guiding his conduct and way of life. It is his duty to practice his profession according to these Canons of Ethics.

As the keystone of professional conduct is integrity, the engineer will discharge his duties with fidelity to the public, his employers and clients, and with fairness and impartiality to all. It is his duty to interest himself in public welfare and to be ready to apply his special knowledge for the benefit of mankind. He should uphold the honor and dignity of his profession and avoid association with any enterprise of questionable character. In his dealings with fellow engineers he should be fair and tolerant.

Professional Life

Canon 1.   The engineer will cooperate in extending the effectiveness of the engineering profession by interchanging information and experience with other engineers and students and by contributing to the work of engineering societies, schools and the scientific and engineering press.

Rule 1.   He will be guided in all his relations by the highest standards.

Rule 2.   He will not lend his name to any enterprise about which he is not thoroughly informed and in which he does not have a positive belief.

Rule 3.   He should seek opportunities to be of constructive service in civic affairs and work for the advancement of the safety, health and well-being of his community.

Rule 4.   He will not offer to pay, either directly or indirectly, any commission, political contribution, or a gift, or other consideration in order to secure work, exclusive of securing salaried positions through employment agencies.

Canon 2.   He will not advertise his work or merit in a self-laudatory manner and he will avoid all conduct or practice likely to discredit or do injury to the dignity and honor of his profession.

Rule 5.   Circumspect advertising may be properly employed by the engineer to announce his practice and availability. The form and manner of such advertising shall satisfy in all respects the dictate and intent of the Canons. Only those media shall be used as are necessary to reach directly an interested and potential client or employer, and such media shall in themselves be dignified, reputable and characteristically free of any factor or circumstance that would bring disrepute to the profession or to the professional using them. The substance of such advertising shall be limited to fact and shall contain no statement or offer intended to discredit or displace another engineer, either specifically or by implication.

Rule 6.   Telephone listings shall be limited to name, address and telephone number under each branch listing in which he qualifies.

Rule 7.   He will not allow himself to be listed for employment using exaggerated statements of his qualifications.

Relations with the Public

Canon 3.   The engineer will endeavor to extend public knowledge of engineering, and will discourage the spreading of untrue, unfair and exaggerated statements regarding engineering.

Rule 8.   He will avoid belittling the necessity for engineering services.

Canon 4.   He will have due regard for the safety of life and health of public and employees who may be affected by the work for which he is responsible.

Rule 9.   He will regard his duty to the public welfare as paramount.

Canon 5.   He will express an opinion only when it is founded on adequate knowledge and honest conviction while he is serving as a witness before a court, commission or other tribunal.

Canon 6.   He will not issue ex parte statements, criticisms or arguments on matters connected with public policy which are inspired or paid for by private interests, unless he indicates on whose behalf he is making the statement.

Rule 10.   He will not advocate or support enactment of community laws, rules, or regulations that he believes are not in the public interest.

Canon 7.   He will refrain from expressing publicly an opinion on an engineering subject unless he is informed as to the facts relating thereto.

Relations with Clients and Employers

Canon 8.   The engineer will act in professional matters for each client or employer as a faithful agent or trustee.

Rule 11.   He will not undertake or agree to perform any engineering service on a free basis.

Rule 12.   He will be conservative and honest in all estimates, reports, statements, and testimony.

Rule 13.   He will advise his client when he believes a project will not be successful.

Rule 14.   His plans or specifications will not be such as to limit free competition, except with his client's consent.

Rule 15.   He will associate himself only with projects of a legitimate character.

Rule 16.   He will not solicit or accept employment to the detriment of his regular work or interest.

Rule 17.   An engineer in private practice may be employed by more than one party when the interests and time schedules of the several parties do not conflict.

Rule 18.   While in the employ of others, he will not enter into promotional efforts or negotiations for work or make arrangements for other employment as a principal or to practice in connection with a specific project for which he has gained particular and specialized knowledge without the consent of all interested parties.

Canon 9.   He will act with fairness and justice between his client or employer and the contractor when dealing with contracts.

Rule 19.   He will insist on contractor compliance with plans and specifications.

Canon 10.   He will make his status clear to his client or employer before undertaking an engagement if he may be called upon to decide on the use of inventions, apparatus, or any other thing in which he may have a financial interest.

Rule 20.   Before undertaking work for others in connection with which he may make improvements, plans, designs, inventions or other records which may justify copyrights or patents, the engineer should enter into a positive agreement regarding the ownership.

Rule 21.   When an engineer or manufacturer builds apparatus from designs supplied to him by a customer, the designs remain the property of the customer and should not be duplicated by the engineer or manufacturers for others without express permission.

Rule 22.   A clear understanding should be reached before the beginning of the work regarding the respective rights of ownership when an engineer or manufacturer and a customer may jointly work out designs and plans or develop inventions.

Rule 23. Designs, data, records, and notes made by an employee and referring exclusively to his employer's work are his employer's property.

Rule 24. A customer, in buying apparatus, does not acquire any right in its design but only the use of the apparatus purchased. A client does not acquire any right to the ideas developed and plans made by a consulting engineer, except for the specific case for which they were made.

Canon 11. He will guard against conditions that are dangerous or threatening to life, limb or property on work for which he is responsible, or if he is not responsible, will promptly call such conditions to the attention of those who are responsible.

Rule 25. He will not complete, sign, or seal plans and/or specifications that are not of a design safe to the public health and welfare. If the client or employer insists on such unprofessional conduct, he shall call building authorities' attention to the case and withdraw from further consulting business or service on the project.

Canon 12. He will present clearly the consequences to be expected from deviations proposed if his engineering judgment is overruled by nontechnical authority in cases where he is responsible for the technical adequacy of engineering work.

Rule 26. He will not apply his signature of approval or seal on plans that do not meet accepted engineering standards.

Canon 13. He will engage, or advise his client or employer to engage, and he will cooperate with, other experts and specialists whenever the client's or employer's interests are best served by such service.

Rule 27. He will not undertake responsible engineering work for which he is not qualified by experience and training.

Canon 14. He will disclose no information concerning the business affairs or technical processes of clients or employers without their consent.

Canon 15. He will not accept compensation, financial or otherwise, from more than one interested party for the same service, or for services pertaining to the same work, without the consent of all interested parties.

Canon 16. He will not accept commissions or allowances, directly or indirectly, from contractors or other parties dealing with his clients or employer in connection with work for which he is responsible.

Rule 28.   He will not accept financial or other considerations, including free engineering designs, from material or equipment suppliers for specifying their product.

Canon 17.   He will not be financially interested in the bids as or of a contractor on competitive work for which he is employed as an engineer unless he has the consent of his client or employer.

Rule 29.   He will not accept personal consideration in any form. This assures that his recommendations for the award of a contract cannot be influenced.

Canon 18.   He will promptly disclose to his client or employer any interest in a business which may compete with or affect the business of his client or employer. He will not allow an interest in any business to affect his decision regarding engineering work for which he is employed, or which he may be called upon to perform.

Relations with Engineers

Canon 19.   The engineer will endeavor to protect the engineering profession collectively and individually from misrepresentation and misunderstanding.

Rule 30.   The engineer will insist on the use of facts in reference to an engineering project or to an engineer in a group discussion, public forum or publication of articles.

Canon 20.   He will take care that credit for engineering work is given to those to whom credit is properly due.

Rule 31.   Whenever possible, he will name the person or persons who may be individually responsible for designs, inventions, writings, or other accomplishments.

Rule 32.   He will not accept by voice or silence, credit rightfully due another engineer.

Rule 33.   He will not sign or seal plans or specifications prepared by someone other than himself or an employee under his supervision

Rule 34.   He will not represent as his own the plans, designs, or specifications supplied to him by a manufacturer or supplier of equipment or material.

Canon 21.   He will uphold the principle of appropriate and ade-

quate compensation for those engaged in engineering work, including those in subordinate capacities, as being in the public interest and maintaining the standards of the profession.

Rule 35. He will not undertake work at a fee or salary that will not permit professional performance, according to accepted standards of the profession.

Rule 36. He will not accept work in the geographic area in which he practices or intends to practice at a salary or fee below that recognized as a basic minimum in that area.

Rule 37. He will not accept remuneration from either an employee or employment agency for giving employment.

Rule 38. When hiring other engineers, he shall offer a salary according to the engineer's qualifications and the recognized standards in the particular geographical area.

Canon 22. He will endeavor to provide opportunity for the professional development and advancement of engineers in his employ.

Rule 39. He will encourage attendance at professional or technical society meetings by his engineer employees.

Rule 40. He should not unduly restrict the preparation and presentation of technical papers by his engineer employees.

Rule 41. He will encourage an employee's efforts to improve his education.

Rule 42. He will urge his engineer employees to become registered at the earliest possible date.

Rule 43. He will assign a professional engineer duties of a nature to utilize his full training and experience, insofar as possible, and delegate lesser functions to subprofessionals or to technicians.

Rule 44. He will not restrain an employee from obtaining a better position with another employer by offers of short-term gains or by belittling the employee's qualifications.

Canon 23. He will not directly or indirectly injure the professional reputation, prospects or practice of another engineer. However, if he considers that an engineer is guilty of unethical, illegal or unfair practice, he will present the information to the proper authority for action.

Rule 45. He will report unethical practices of another engineer with substantiating data to his professional or technical society, and be willing to appear as a witness.

Canon 24. He will exercise due restraint in criticizing another *engineer's work in public, recognizing the fact that the engineering societies and the engineering press provide the proper forum for technical discussions and criticism.*

Rule 46.   He will not review the work of another engineer for the same client, except with the knowledge or consent of such engineer, or unless the connection of such engineer with the work has been terminated.

Canon 25.   He will not try to supplant another engineer in a particular employment after becoming aware that definite steps have been taken toward the other's employment.

Rule 47.   He will not attempt to inject his services into a project at the expense of another engineer who has been active in developing it.

Canon 26.   He will not compete with another engineer an the basis of charges for work by underbidding, through reducing his normal fees after having been informed of the charges named by the other.

Rule 48.   The practice of engineering is a learned profession, requiring of its members sound technical training, broad experience, personal ability, honesty and integrity. The selection of engineering services by an evaluation of these qualities should be the basis of comparison rather than competitive bids.

Rule 49.   Competition between engineers for employment on the basis of professional fees or charges is considered unethical practice by all professional engineering groups. Any engineer who is requested to submit a competitive bid to an owner or a governmental body should remove himself from consideration for the proposed work.

Rule 50.   It shall be considered ethical for an engineer to solicit an engineering assignment, either verbally or written. Such solicitation may be in the form of a letter or a brochure setting forth factual information concerning the engineer's qualifications by training and experience and reference to past accomplishments and clients.

Should the engineer be asked for a proposal to perform engineering services for a specific project, he should set forth in detail the work he proposes to accomplish and an indication of the calendar days required for its accomplishment. The engineer's qualifications may be included if appropriate. A statement of monetary remuneration expected shall be avoided until he has been selected for the proposed work.

Should the owner insist upon a statement regarding remuneration prior to selection of the engineer, the engineer may designate the recognized professional society minimum fee schedule for the particular type of service required in the state geographical area where the work is to be done.

Rule 51. He will take a professional attitude in negotiations for his services and shall avoid all practices which have a tendency to affect adversely the amount,. quality, or disinterested nature of professional services; such as charging inadequate fees for preliminary work or full services, competing for an engineering assignment on a price basis, spending large amounts of money in securing business or consenting to furnish monetary guarantees of cost estimates.

Canon 27. He will not use the advantages of a salaried position to compete unfairly with another engineer.

Rule 52. While in a salaried position, he will accept part-time engineering work only at a salary or fee not less than that recognized as standard in the area.

Rule 53. An engineer will not use equipment, supplies, laboratory, or office facilities of his employer to carry on outside private practice without consent.

Canon 28. He will not become associated in responsibility for work with engineers who do not conform to ethical practices.

Rule 54. He will conform with registration laws in his practice of engineering.

Rule 55. He will not use association with a non-engineer, a corporation, or partnership, as a "cloak" for unethical acts; but must accept personal responsibility for his professional acts.

Miscellaneous

Rule 56. An engineer who is in sales or industrial employ is entitled to make engineering comparisons of the products offered by various suppliers, but will avoid aspersions upon their character, standing, or ability.

Rule 57. If, in sales employ, he will not offer, or give engineering consultation, or designs, or advice other than specifically applying to the operation of the equipment being sold.

Rule 58. No engineer in the employ of equipment or material supply companies will tender designs, plans, specifications, advice or consultation to operations beyond the limits of a machine or item of material or supply, except as is required for proper functioning of the particular item.

Rule 59.   He will not use his professional affiliations to secure the confidence of other engineers in commercial enterprise and will avoid any act tending to promote his own interest at the expense of the dignity and standing of the profession.

Rule 60.   He will admit and accept his own errors when proven obviously wrong and refrain from distorting or altering the facts in an attempt to justify his decision.

Rule 61.   Any firm offering engineering services must, in conformance with the laws of the state in which it operates, have its operations under the direction and responsibility of registered professional engineers.

Rule 62.   He will not attempt to attract an engineer from another employer by methods such as offering unjustified salaries or benefits.

*   *   *

Procedures for handling individual cases of ethical misconduct and legal infractions of the professional registration laws vary from society to society and state to state. The Florida Engineering Society, an affiliate of the National Society of Professional Engineers, has formalized a procedure for handling alleged professional misconduct. This procedure is reprinted below, by permission, as an example of means used to consider cases which may result in such severe penalties as expulsion from the Society or revocation of professional registration:

PROCEDURE TO BE USED BY THE CONSULTING ENGINEERS OF FLORIDA IN HANDLING ALLEGED PROFESSIONAL MISCONDUCT AFFECTING THE PRACTICE OF ENGINEERING

PREAMBLE

The purpose of this report is to establish an orderly procedure whereby the Consulting Engineers of Florida, a functional section of the Florida Engineering Society, may assist the Florida Engineering Society Ethical Practices Committee and pertinent local Chapter committees in reviewing cases of ethical misconduct and legal infractions in accordance with the Registration Law and the Canons of Ethics; and further, to establish an Engineering Board of Review appointed by the Consulting Engineers of Florida Administrative Committee, to review alleged acts of incompetence.

The areas of professional conduct which are subject to review are as follows:

1. Unethical Practices 2. Legal Infractions 3. Incompetence

COMPLAINTS

Complaints shall be made in writing to the Florida Engineering Society, attention Executive Director, 1906 Lee Rd, Orlando, Florida. The complaint should include sufficient information to allow the appropriate committee to take further action.

Upon receipt of the complaint, the Executive Director will evaluate the complaint and refer it to the appropriate committee, either the Ethical Practices Committee of the Florida Engineering Society, or the Professional Practices Committee of the Consulting Engineers of Florida.

SECTION I—ETHICAL MISCONDUCT AND LEGAL INFRACTION

The purpose of this section is to establish an orderly procedure to be used by the Consulting Engineers of Florida in assisting the Florida Engineering Society Ethical Practices Committee and the pertinent local committees with regard to ethical misconduct and legal infraction.

A. *Professional Practices Committee.* The committee designated to carry out the procedures provided for in this report with regard to ethical misconduct and legal infractions shall be the Professional Practices Committee of the Consulting Engineers of Florida. Each member will take an oath that he will, fairly and impartially and to the best of his ability, administer the work of this committee.

B. *Secretary.* The Professional Practices Committee shall select one of its members as Secretary, who shall keep minutes of the proceedings of the committee.

C. *Investigations.* The Committee shall have the power by written complaint to investigate in a formal or informal manner any professional misconduct alleged to have been committed by any person. The Professional Practices Committee may refer the investigation to an existing Chapter committee of the Florida Engineering Society, and if a committee is not in operation, may appoint a local committee to assist in the informal investigation. If, upon any such investigation, a majority of the members of the committee finds that there is reasonable cause to believe that the accused is guilty of professional misconduct, the committee shall cause, with prior approval of the Administrative Committee of the Consulting Engineers of Florida, a formal preliminary hearing to be held.

D. *Hearings.*   Advance notice of two weeks shall be given the accused prior to his hearing by the CEOF Professional Practices Committee. The accused shall be heard in his own defense, and may be represented by legal counsel at his own expense, and produce evidence to refute the charges.

E. *Notice of Hearing.*   The Chairman of the Professional Practices Committee shall send a notice of the hearing to the accused by registered mail, addressed to his last known residence or business address. The notice shall include a full description of the complaint and/or charges against him, the time and place of which he may be heard.

F. *Results of Hearing.*   If, after such formal hearing by the Professional Practices Committee, or upon refusal or failure of the accused to appear for a hearing, a majority of the members of the committee finds that there is sufficient cause to believe the accused is guilty of the misconduct charge, it shall, with the approval of the CEOF Administrative Committee, cause to be taken one of the following corrective measures, whichever is appropriate:

a) *Legal Infraction.*   In the instance of the apparent violation, by the individual charged, of the Florida State statute, the case shall be referred to the State Board of Engineer Examiners without recommendation, including certificated evidence of the findings of the Professional Practices Committee.

b) *Unethical Practices.*   In the instance of apparent unethical conduct by the individual charged as set forth in the Canons of Ethics and Rules of Professional Conduct for Engineers, the case shall be referred to the Florida Engineering Society Ethical Practices Committee with recommendations. The Florida Engineering Society Ethical Practices Committee shall make final recommendations to the Board of Directors of FES, and may or may not accept the recommendations made by the Professional Practices Committee of the Consulting Engineers of Florida.

c) If, in the opinion of the Professional Practices Committee, the accused is guilty of both a legal infraction and an unethical practice, the case shall be referred to the Ethical Practices Committee of the Florida Engineering Society, with additional information for their files when they review the case.

G. *Counsel.*   The work of the Professional Practices Committee, when the need warrants, shall be with the advice of an attorney employed by the Consulting Engineers of Florida.

H. *Appeals.*   The accused, if he believes he has received unjust treatment, may appeal to the Board of Directors of the Florida Engineering Society.

I. *Form of Notice.*   The official notice of the hearing shall be filed by the chairman of the Professional Practices Committee. The notice to the accused shall be submitted in the following form:

Consulting Engineers of Florida
Professional Practices Committee

The Professional Practices Committee of the Consulting Engineers of Florida, in accordance with the policy established by the Florida Engineering Society, and with the knowledge and approval of the Administrative Committee of the Consulting Engineers of Florida, hereby requests you to appear before it on the ___ day of _____ 19___, at _____ for the purpose of answering accusations that you have allegedly violated the following:

(Describe complaint in full here)

The proceedings at this preliminary hearing will be in the strictest confidence as established by the Florida Engineering Society, and the spirit of the hearing will be one of friendliness and helpfulness. By order of the Professional Practices committee of the Consulting Engineers of Florida.

BY _____
Chairman

Date of Notice: _____

J. *Extension of Time.*   For good cause shown, the Professional Practices Committee may extend or continue any hearing.

SECTION II—INCOMPETENCE

The purpose of this section is to establish an orderly procedure whereby the engineering profession within itself can aid in improving the quality of engineering in the State of Florida in the spirit of friendly helpfulness to all registered professional engineers licensed by the State of Florida.

A. *Engineering Board of Review* (hereafter referred to as *Board of Review*). In instances of an alleged act of incompetence by written complaint, engineering plans and specifications relating to the complaint shall be reviewed at the direction of the Consulting Engineers of Florida Administrative Committee, by a Board of Review which shall be appointed as needed to review specific cases. The Board of Review shall be appointed by the CEOF Administrative Committee and shall consist of not less than three professional engineers who shall be registered in Florida, and who are especially and technically qualified to judge the competence of the plans and specifications in question. It is not necessary that the members of the Board of Review be members of CEOF or FES. Members of the Board of Review shall be willing to testify in court with respect to their findings. All records and reports shall be strictly confidential between the members of the Board of Review and the concerned engineer, and shall be kept on file in the State Headquarters of FES.

B. *Chairman and Secretary.* Each Board of Review shall select one of its members as chairman and one as secretary, who shall keep minutes of the proceedings of the board.

C. *Board of Review Procedure.* If, upon review, a majority of the members of the Board of Review finds that there is reasonable cause to believe the accused is incompetent to the degree of endangering the life, health, property and welfare of the public, the Board of Review shall prepare a Report of Review which shall include specific points of incompetence found in the work reviewed. Said Report of Review shall be presented to the accused either by the committee or its representative or by registered mail to the last known address of the accused.

At the request of the accused, a hearing will be held between the Board of Review and the accused, the time and place of the hearing to be established by the Board of Review after consulting with the accused. If, after such hearing by the Board of Review, or upon refusal or failure of the accused to appear for a hearing or to submit evidence to refute the charges made against him, the Board of Review will submit their findings to the CEOF Administrative Committee. The Administrative Committee, with the consent of the Florida Engineering Society Executive Committee shall refer the matter to the State Board of Engineer Examiners with recommendations. The Florida Engineering Society will advise the accused of the action taken.

D. *Expenses.* Expenses incurred by members of the Board of Review in performance of their official duties may be paid by the CEOF. Said expenses shall be limited to transportation, meals, and lodging.

E. *Counsel.* The work of the Board of Review, when the need warrants, shall be with the advice of an attorney, employed by the CEOF for this purpose.

F. *Appeals.* The accused, if he believes he has received unjust treatment, may within thirty days appeal to the Board of Directors of the Florida Engineering Society, who shall give full and impartial consideration to the appeal.

* * *

Ethical practices, however, should be much more concerned with the positive approach of encouraging and aiding correct ethical action, rather than the negative approach of penalizing misconduct. The written *Canons of Ethics* is the beginning of this positive approach; but there remains the major complex task of interpreting and applying correctly the written *Canons* and of coping satisfactorily with the many problems which are not clearly covered or specifically mentioned in the *Canons of Ethics.* The complexity of this task of interpretation is particularly evident in the instance of the American Bar Association *Canons of Professional Ethics* consisting of 47 Canons for which, as listed in Appendix A of Drinker's text (1), there have been 383 "Decisions by the American Bar Association Ethics Committee Hitherto Unreported" interpreting the Canons. Drinker's text on legal ethics, in addition, devotes most of its 448 pages to the presentation of actual legal cases and rulings interpreting the Canons.

Most of the engineering societies have also, from time to time, published specific interpretations of their codes of ethics. The National Society of Professional Engineers has established a special Board of Ethical Review to render impartial opinions pertaining to the interpretation of the *Canons of Ethics.* Findings of the Board of Ethical Review on specific cases have been reported periodically in the *American Engineer* (see assignments at end of this chapter). It is to be expected that an individual with broad experience and tested judgment is most likely to come forth with the correct or best solution to a problem; and that the joint thinking of a group of such individuals would probably represent the best contemporary reasoning—such would be the purpose of a Board of Ethical Review. The reasoning process is facilitated by using the organized methodology of engineering (illustrative examples of the methodology, as applied to ethics, are shown in the following section).

3-9 PROBLEMS IN ENGINEERING ETHICS.

Ethical problems discussed in this text are limited primarily to those related to the practice of engineering. This has been done because, as a beginning, it is easier to cope with the narrower area close to oneself; and also one should clean up his own house before considering larger areas. Ethical problems become no less complex when a solution is undertaken by an adaptation of the methodology of engineering, herein referred to as a "methodology of ethics," (see Fig. 3-1), but one should thus be better able to cope with them. The methodology should aid in uprooting haziness, self-centeredness, self-deception, and dependence on authority to develop the rational processes, form a sound set of personal values, and increase the ability to arrive at one's own correct conclusions.

Most assigned problems in engineering texts and classroom are organized so that it is necessary only to use part of the methodology, usually merely to carry the problem through the deductive process to obtain the prediction or answers. Economics and time usually do not allow taking each problem through the production or construction stage, while in the engineering school. The young, inexperienced engineering graduate is not likely to be given the responsibility to make appraisals leading to a decision to produce or prevent in an important project; and therefore the appraisal step in the methodology is also usually omitted in classroom engineering problems. However, even the inexperienced young graduate must make major ethical decisions for himself frequently; and therefore it is vital that practice problems in ethics be carried through at least to the appraisal and decision step.

The appraisal step in the solution of an engineering problem might include asking typical questions such as: Will it work? Is it safe? Will it pay? Why do it this way? Why do it now? Why do it at all? The probability of having a good appraisal for a specific problem may be increased by (a) increasing the number of qualified people participating in the appraisal and obtaining consistency of opinion, *(b)* allowing a lapse of time and later reappraisal, *(c)* evaluation of previous appraisals of similar problems, after production or prevention. The value judgments which enter into the appraisal of an engineering problem are in no way as precise and as clear cut as are the calculations involved in analysis and design. Although appraisal questions are complex and difficult to answer, the practicing engineer must answer them every day. Review of some specific appraisal questions related to an engineering design problem should demonstrate that this aspect of an engineering problem is often more intangible, involves more metaphysics (assumptions) and comprehensive judgment than many ethical problems (as illustrated later in this section). As an example the following are appraisal questions which an engineer might want to answer after he had completed a preliminary design (predictions) and cost estimates for a steel truss bridge having as a purpose the carrying of automobiles across a river, prior to completing the design and having the construction start. Answering of the last two questions would require either previous experience with similar problems or new designs (predictions) for the alternative solutions:

Appraisal Questions

1. Can the construction costs of the bridge be financed?
2. Is the bridge safe?
3. Is the bridge functional and aesthetic?
4. Will the necessary materials be available when needed?
5. Are qualified construction personnel and equipment available?
6. Are qualified inspectors available during the construction period?
7. Are finances and qualified personnel available for maintenance?
8. Can the bridge be completed by the given deadline?
9. Is the given deadline realistic and appropriate?
10. Does the bridge hinder present or future use of the river?
11. Can the bridge also serve other purposes such as carrying pipelines and powerlines across the river?

12. Have adequate considerations been given to future increases in traffic flow and modernization?
13. Does the bridge tie in satisfactorily with existing and planned access roads?
14. Should construction be delayed until next year when a new, more economical steel alloy is expected to be available?
15. Should construction be delayed until a new design code is adopted, which may result in economies in construction?
16. Should the bridge not be built at all, letting traffic use an existing bridge farther down the river?
17. Should the design life of the bridge be changed to bring the actual cost closer to available finances.
18. Would it be "better" (in terms of cost, durability, aesthetics, time of availability, etc.) to use another type of bridge made out of other materials?
19. Would it be "better" to use other means such as a tunnel or ferry to fulfill the purpose?

Many basic engineering problems, such as establishing a factor of safety or a design life (the period of anticipated efficient utility), have major overtones in ethical areas. The partial solution of Example 3-1 illustrates how the Utilitarian Principle might be used to give predictions of the consequences of increasing the design life of automobiles, which may then be appraised as to whether or not this increase in design life is good and to what extent. Note that additional assumptions are added in order to assist in categorizing the advantages and disadvantages. Assumptions of being advantageous, or consequences which are advantages, would be that which is anticipated to promote the Utilitarian Principle of bringing the greatest amount of happiness to the greatest number of people over the greatest period of time. In the appraisal, some scale of values would have to be placed upon each assumption and each consequence. The assignment of this scale of values may involve the solution of new ethical problems; or evaluation of previously solved problems may serve as criteria for the scale of values.

Example 3-2A shows a solution to an ethical problem, employing the Utilitarian Principle, carried through to the decision stage. Example 3-2B illustrates those portions of the same problem which differ when the Universal Law (Kant's Categorical Imperative) is employed in the solution. Similarly, Examples 3-3 and 3-4 illustrate solutions employing both the Utilitarian Principle and the Universal Law. Example 3-5 is solved by the Utilitarian Principle.

A number of different principles (discussed in this text) may be used for the deductive process in the method of ethical analysis including:

a) Utilitarian Principle—Seek consequences which will bring the greatest amount of happiness to the greatest number of people over the greatest period of time.
b) Universal Law (Kant's categorical imperative)—Consider the consistency with purposes and assumptions if everyone was to do as you propose to do.
c) The Golden Rule—Do unto others as you would have them do unto you.
d) Aristotle's Doctrine of the Golden Mean—Moral virtue is a mean between two vices, the one involving excess, the other deficiency.
e) Sidgwick's Maxim of Justice—Whatever is right for one person, is right for all similar persons in similar circumstances.

Each engineering principle or equation is applicable, or can be used with greater facility, only with certain types of problems. Similarly, specific ethical principles are more appropriate for certain types of ethical problems. The Universal Law, as may particularly be noted in Examples 3-2 and 3-3, tends to indicate more simple and clear cut predictions and appraisals for ethical problems involving a yes or no type of decision. On the other hand, the Utilitarian Principles is most effective where there are a large number or a range of alternatives all of which are

Example 3-1

ASSUMED (CIRCUMSTANCES) FACTS

The design life of automobiles is to be increased.

Selection

METHOD OF ETHICAL ANALYSIS—UTILITARIAN
PRINCIPLE

Assumptions:

1. It is advantageous to keep as many people as possible in productive instead of non-productive occupations.
2. It is advantageous to facilitate means of transportation.
3. It is advantageous to increase safety.
4. It is advantageous to make gainful employment available to all.
5. Increase in design life would increase initial cost and safety.
6. The automobiles are to continue to be mass produced and to compete in international markets.

Deduction

PREDICTIONS—CONSEQUENCES

Advantages	*Disadvantages*
1. Annual cost of operation and fixed charges would be less.	1. Incentive for technological advances and incorporation of technological advances would be reduced.
2. Natural resources would be conserved.	2. Total employment in the auto industry would drop.
3. Smaller sales staff would be needed, thus decreasing the percentage of non-productive workers in the industry.	3. Down payments (on higher priced autos) would probably increase.
4. Increase in safety.	4. Additional capital will be necessary to finance a major change.

Example 3-1 (Continued)
Estimates | Appraisal

APPRAISAL QUESTIONS

1. Does the state of the economy require more openings for employment?
2. Is there over or undercapacity of the major materials used in autos?
3. What percentage of people would be able to cope with larger down payments?
4. Is it advantageous to limit car ownership through high down payments in order to promote the use of mass transport; or is it preferable to encourage automobile ownership for all and cope with traffic congestion by control of location and time of use (e.g., public support of mass transport, instead of highway access, to congested areas)?
5. What would be the effect upon imports and exports of automobiles?
6. What would be the near- and far-term effects upon the used car market?
7. Can one manufacturer alone radically change the design life and still compete?
8. How often would model changes (each having the longer design life) be presented?
9. Are finances available for a major change in design life (e.g., for retooling, redesign, etc.)?
10. Can the lower annual proportionate spending for automobiles support the required capital?
11. Are these capital outlays greater than those required for frequent style changes?
12. Would the average person keep their automobiles longer; or would each automobile just become available to a greater number of successive used car buyers, over a longer period of time?
13. What have been the market and public attitudes toward automobiles such as the Rolls Royce which have been designed for relatively long life?
14. What would be the effect upon the "2-car" and "3-car" families?
15. Does the trend toward more hours of leisure dictate a need for greater availability of automobiles?

DECISION TO PRODUCE OR PREVENT
?

acceptable; or in certain instances it may be necessary to choose the best of several alternatives, all undesirable to a greater or lesser extent. The Golden Rule and the Maxim of Justice tend to be easier to use in a yes or no type of problem, while the Golden

Example 3-2A

RECOGNITION OF PROBLEM

A manufacturing company offered a consulting engineer a commission of 10% of the cost of their material used on his client's job, provided the engineer specified their brand of material. If the engineer knew or believed that the material was equal in quality to similar material on the market and would not cost more than similar materials, ought he to accept the commission?

Determination

ASSUMED (CIRCUMSTANCES) FACTS

The engineer accepts the 10% commission.

Selection

METHOD OF ETHICAL ANALYSIS—UTILITARIAN PRINCIPLE

Assumptions:

1. A consulting engineer is in a position of trust with the primary responsibility of preparing a safe, functioning design which can be produced at lowest cost for the efficiency and durability desired by the client, and at the time needed.
2. The consulting engineer will be fairly compensated by the client for the effort and time expended in performing his duties; and the consulting engineer will expend a reasonable amount of time in preparing the design, recognizing that the cost of additional study of the engineering design should not exceed the potential savings on production (assuming safety is not sacrificed).
3. It is advantageous to avoid monopoly and to maintain a free economy, subject to meeting the needs and desires of the ultimate consumer.

Example 3-2A (Continued)

Deduction

PREDICTIONS—CONSEQUENCES

Advantages	*Disadvantages*
1. Additional income for the engineer.	1. Elimination of equal opportunity for other manufacturers, tending to monopolistic control, future lowering of quality, and raising of prices.
2. Additional business for the manufacturer offering the commission.	2. Risks injury of the reputation of the engineer and his position as a consultant.
3. Ordering of material is simplified.	3. Creates future obligations to the manufacturer offering the commission.
	4. Makes it easier to accept other commissions in instances where material and prices are not equal to that of the competition.
	5. Creates tendency to "overspecify" on all work and to raise costs.
	6. Engineer now serves two masters, the client and the manufacturer.
	7. Loss of peace of mind through concern about others finding out; or, even if one had rationalized the situation for themselves, there would be worry about interpretation by others.

Estimates | Appraisal

⟶

Example 3-2A (Continued)

APPRAISAL QUESTIONS

1. If the manufacturing company can give a 10% commission (for no real contribution) could they not lower their selling price instead?
2. What is the probability of the client finding out about the commission; and what would be his attitude (e.g., will the client be likely to believe that quality and cost are the same as other brands?)?
3. What is the possibility of other clients, engineers, and manufacturers finding out about the commission, and what would be their attitude?
4. What is the possible effect upon the engineer's reputation and what is the potential loss in lifetime income, if his reputation is injured?
5. How does the possible loss in lifetime income compare in magnitude with the commission offered?
6. What is the effect upon the engineer's family and upon the profession at large if scandal occurs?
7. Is accepting the commission in conflict with the duties of an engineer to his client?
8. Is the commission likely to influence the engineer's judgement relative to the quality of the manufacturers products?
9. Is this a commission (money received for selling) or a bribe (money received for the use of undue influence)?
10. Should the manufacturer be requested to offer the 10% commission directly to the client? Note, this question presents another alternative to the mere personal acceptance or rejection of the commission; and consideration of this alternative would require the solution of a new problem.
11. Are the Canons of Ethics (e.g., 15, 16, or 17) applicable?

DECISION TO PRODUCE OR PREVENT

The engineer should not accept the commission for his personal use.

Mean applies to the selection from a range of choices. Quite a few ethical theories, not covered in this text, can also be used; but the author believes that the Utilitarian Principle and the Universal Law are the ones which can be used most objectively and successfully in the methodology.

Example 3-2B

METHOD OF ETHICAL ANALYSIS—UNIVERSAL LAW

Assumptions:

(Same as Example 3-2A)

Deduction

PREDICTION—UNIVERSALITIES

1. Accepting the commission sanctions a society in which all people could receive compensations without making any productive contribution. (Note assumption that the engineer is already compensated for his efforts by the client.)
2. If all people in positions of influence could specify the brand of all purchases, this would lead to a condition where all businesses would seek to please only those with influence, and not the ultimate consumer.
3. If all specifications listed one and the same manufacturer, this would create a monopolistic empire.

Estimates | Appraisal

APPRAISAL QUESTIONS

1. Are the universal conditions predicted consistent with purposes, assumptions, and accepted standards of conduct (e.g., Canons of Ethics 8, 15, 16, or 17)?
2. Are there other alternatives such as requesting that the 10% commission be offered directly to the client (a new solution and predictions of universalities would be needed to appraise the other alternatives)?

DECISION TO PRODUCE OR PREVENT

The engineer should not accept the commission for his personal use.

Example 3-3A

RECOGNITION OF PROBLEM

A manufacturing company offered an engineer owner of a contracting firm a commission of 10% of the cost of their material if he would specify their material with his bid on a client's proposed job. If the engineer knew or believed that the material was equal in quality to similar material on the market and that its basic cost is no more than similar materials, ought he to accept the commission?

Determination

ASSUMED (CIRCUMSTANCES) FACTS

The engineer accepts the 10% commission.

Selection

METHOD OF ETHICAL ANALYSIS—UTILITARIAN PRINCIPLE

Assumptions:

1. The primary responsibility of a contractor is to produce, in accordance with plans and specifications, at the lowest possible cost plus a fair compensation (profit) for his effort and time.
2. Several contractors are competent to perform the work and desire to submit competitive bids for the job.
3. The contractor submitting the lowest bid will be awarded the contract to perform the work.
4. Each contractor will submit the lowest possible bid, consistent with his actual costs plus a fair profit, in order to increase the probability of his obtaining the job.
5. The availability of lower selling and bid prices allows a society to use its resources more efficiently, and a greater number of people can thereby afford to undertake desired projects.
6. The client can elect to refuse all bids if he is not satisfied with the costs or specified materials.

Deduction

Example 3-3A (Continued)

PREDICTIONS—CONSEQUENCES

Advantages	*Disadvantages*
1. Acceptance of the commission has the effect of lowering the engineer-contractor's actual cost, thus allowing him to submit a lower bid.	1. Other manufacturers have decreased probability of making the sale.
2. Client will obtain the desired work at a lower price.	
3. The manufacturer offering the commission increases the probability of his making the sale.	
4. Tend to make other manufacturers lower their selling prices.	

Estimates | Appraisal

APPRAISAL QUESTIONS

1. What is the extent of increased probability of the engineer obtaining the job if he accepts the commission and lowers his bid accordingly?
2. Could the engineer benefit from the offer of the commission if he was not the low bidder and therefore had no reason to use the material?
3. Is this a commission (money received for selling) or a discount (a reduction in price given as an inducement to purchase)? Note that actions are often given titles having connotations entirely inconsistent with the facts.
4. Is the offering and accepting of *discounts* consistent with the functioning of our society?
5. Are the Canons of Ethics (e.g., 8, 15, 16 or 17) applicable?

DECISION TO PRODUCE OR PREVENT

The engineer-contractor should accept the 10% commission (for the purpose of submitting a lower bid).

Example 3-3B

METHOD OF ETHICAL ANALYSIS—UNIVERSAL LAW

Assumptions:

(Same as example 3-3A)

Deduction

PREDICTIONS—UNIVERSALITIES

1. If all manufacturers gave the maximum possible commissions (discounts which are consistent with efficient operations and a reasonable profit) and all contractors submitted the lowest possible bids (consistent with their actual costs plus a fair profit), the maximum amount of goods and services would become available to society.

Estimates | Appraisal

APPRAISAL QUESTIONS

1. Are the universal conditions predicted consistent with purposes, assumptions and accepted standards of conduct (e.g., Canons of Ethics 15, 16 or 17)?

DECISION TO PRODUCE OR PREVENT

The engineer-contractor should accept the 10% commission (for the purpose of submitting a lower bid).

Example 3-4A

RECOGNITION OF THE PROBLEM

An engineer is given the responsibility of recommending the purchase of some costly machinery to be used by his firm. He is very familiar with the available machinery from all but one of the manufacturers believed to produce the quality of equipment needed. This one manufacturer, wishing to receive equal consideration, offered to pay all the expenses of a trip to their plant and to several places where their equipment was in use. The engineer desired this information and could find time for the trip. Should he pay his own way, accept the expense paid invitation, or just eliminate that manufacturer from consideration?

Determination

ASSUMED (CIRCUMSTANCES) FACTS

The engineer accepts the expense paid trip.

Selection

METHOD OF ETHICAL ANALYSIS—UTILITARIAN PRINCIPLE

Assumptions:

1. It is advantageous for the engineer to choose the machinery upon the basis of the maximum readily available knowledge.
2. It is advantageous for the manufacturer to make others aware of the merits of their products.
3. The engineer should be impartial and free of obligations when choosing the machinery.

Deduction

Example 3-4A (Continued)

PREDICTIONS—CONSEQUENCES

Advantages

1. The engineer will gain greater knowledge of the available machinery.
2. The manufacturer gains equal consideration of their machinery.
3. The engineer increases the probability of obtaining the best machinery at the lowest price.

Disadvantages

1. Expense to the manufacturer.
2. The engineer may feel obligated to the manufacturer.
3. The engineer loses the time expended on the trip.

Estimates | Appraisal

APPRAISAL QUESTIONS

1. Is advertising necessary in our economy; and is this a form of advertising?
2. What is the best form of advertising for complicated, costly machinery?
3. Should an engineer feel any obligation for receiving free advertising information? Is it worth his spending time to obtain this information?
4. What is the probability of this machinery being the best for the price? Does this probability justify the time to be expended for the trip?
5. Can the engineer discharge his responsibility adequately without the full information?
6. Are there other and better ways of becoming informed about the machinery?
7. Are the Canons of Ethics (e.g., 8, 13, 15, 16, 17) applicable?

DECISION TO PRODUCE OR PREVENT

(*Assumption:* There is high probability of this machinery being best for the price.)

The engineer should accept the expense paid trip.

Example 3-4B

METHOD OF ETHICAL ANALYSIS—UNIVERSAL
LAW

Assumptions:

(Same as Example 3-4A)

Deduction

PREDICTIONS—UNIVERSALITIES

1. Universal application for manufacturers would lead to conditions where all manufacturers gave adequate factual information to all people responsible for the selection of products.
2. All engineers would obtain the maximum of readily available information before recommending purchases.

Estimates | Appraisal

APPRAISAL QUESTIONS

1. Are the universal conditions predicted consistent with purpose, assumptions, and accepted standards of conduct (e.g., Canons of Ethics 8, 13, 15, 16, 17)?

DECISION TO PRODUCE OR PREVENT

The engineer should accept the expense paid trip.

Mistakes in engineering problems most commonly occur in the deductive process (mathematics), in wrong assumptions which result in overlooking limitations of the theory, and in the use of poor judgment at the appraisal stage. Similarly, mistakes, or different answers, in ethical problems are most likely to occur in the deductive process where important predictions (e.g., consequences) may be overlooked, when inconsistent assumptions or presuppositions (assumptions of which, one is *not* aware) are used, and when poor judgment is used in the appraisal. In addition, two sources of mistakes and confusion ordinarily considered quite carefully in engineering problems: agreement upon the observed facts, and definitions involved, are very frequently troublesome in ethical problems.

The first requisite for being ethical is having the desire to be ethical. If one understands that ethics involves the seeking of fulfillment of purpose, of seeking the greatest good, of not sacrificing the greater good for the lesser, then there can be no other logical choice than to be ethical. The engineer who can apply the methodology of engineering well in his daily professional practice should also be able to use this same organized approach to determine what he "ought to do" to find the good life.

Example 3-5

RECOGNITION OF THE PROBLEM

If the engineer accepts the invitation and necessary expenses are paid for his trip as discussed in Example 3-4A, should he also accept costly entertainment and gifts, side trips for pleasure, or minor favors (e.g., a cigarette, an inexpensive, unrelated long distance phone call, the morning newspaper, etc.)? If only some ought to be accepted, how and where is the line drawn?

Determination

Example 3-5 (Continued)

ASSUMED (CIRCUMSTANCES) FACTS

The engineer accepts all offerings of costly entertainment and gifts, side trips for pleasure, and minor favors.

Selection

↓

METHOD OF ETHICAL ANALYSIS—UTILITARIAN PRINCIPLE

Assumptions:

(Same as Example 3-4A)

Deduction

↓

PREDICTIONS—CONSEQUENCES
(Related primarily to the assumed facts of this Example)

Advantages	*Disadvantages*
1. The engineer may enjoy the gifts and entertainment.	1. Additional expense to the manufacturer.
2. The manufacturer may create a feeling of obligation and thereby gain a sale.	2. The engineer may feel obligated and therefore not choose the machinery impartially.
	3. Receiving personal compensation from the manufacturer has the engineer in the position of serving two masters.
	4. Risks injury of the reputation of the engineer and his position with his own firm. Manufacturer's reputation may also be injured.
	5. Each gift accepted makes the taking of the next (larger gift) easier, the receiving of something for nothing becoming the norm.

Example 3-5 (Continued)

Estimates | Appraisal

APPRAISAL QUESTIONS

1. Are the gifts, favors, and entertainment necessary for the proper functioning of the relations between the engineer and the manufacturer?
2. Could not the firm sell the machinery to the engineer's firm at a lower price if their unnecessary expenditures are eliminated?
3. What is the probability of the engineer's firm finding out about the gifts and entertainment, and what would be their attitude (e.g., are they likely to believe that an impartial judgment was made and the machinery obtained at the lowest possible price)?
4. What is the probability of other engineers and manufacturers finding out about the gifts and entertainment, and what would be their attitude?
5. What is the possible effect upon the engineer's reputation and what is the potential loss in lifetime income if his reputation is injured?
6. How does the possible loss of lifetime income compare with the value of the gifts and entertainment?
7. What is the effect upon the engineer's family and upon the profession at large if scandal occurs?
8. Does acceptance of the gifts and entertainment create a feeling of obligation which may make the engineer partial?
9. Is the refusing of the offer of minor favors such as a cigarette or a newspaper an unnecessary inconvenience and a discourteous reaction to sincere hospitality?
10. Is the offering of costly gifts and entertainment a normal display of sincere hospitality by casual friends?
11. What is difference between a "gift" and a "bribe"?
12. Are people sometimes given bribes to obtain preferential treatment only upon those occasions when the preferential treatment may not appear too obvious to others?
13. Are the Canons of Ethics (e.g., 8, 13, 15, 16, 17) applicable?

Example 3-5 (Continued)

DECISION TO PRODUCE OR PREVENT

Actions may range from:

(a) Refuse all favors, gifts and expenses except those deemed necessary for the primary purpose (this approach is the simplest and easiest to apply consistently; it is preferable to err on the conservative side).

(b) Accept only such minor favors as would normally be offered by and accepted from casual friends (e.g., a casual friend would be unlikely to offer a gift of a mink coat for one's wife) which would be unlikely to create a feeling of obligation, or create suspicion by others that there has not been impartial treatment.

ASSIGNMENTS

3.1 Define the following in the context of ethical discourse:

a)	Expert	j)	Patriotism
b)	Progress	k)	Security
c)	Power	l)	Utopia
d)	Originality	m)	Tolerance
e)	Civilization	n)	Ambition
f)	Democracy	o)	Luck
g)	Citizenship	p)	Belief
h)	Government	q)	Patience
i)	Fashion	r)	Sacrifice

Show a complete schematic solution, through the Decision step of the Methodology of Ethics for the cases or problems below. Use for the method of Ethical Analysis (A) Utilitarian Principle (B) Universal Law.

The following group of assignments are cases which have been reported upon by the National Society of Professional Engineer's Board of Ethical Review in various issues of the *American Engineer*. These cases are reprinted with permission. Answers to each case, given by the Board of Ethical Review, may be found in the issue of the *American Engineer (A.E.)* indicated at the end of each case.

3.2 Facts: Engineer "A" had been retained by an Owner for certain engineering services under written agreement. Prior to the completion of his work, "A" was notified by the Owner that his services were being terminated. Subsequently, Engineer "B" was retained by the Owner for the same work. Engineer "B" was notified by Engineer "A" that the termination of his service was by unilateral action of the Owner and was not "accepted" by Engineer "A".

Question: Was it ethical conduct on "B's" part to accept the contract in view of the unilateral termination of "A's" services without his consent, and over his objection?

(*A.E.,* May, 1960. p. 39)

3.3 Facts: A consulting engineer prepared the following specification for a project:

"The design of members and connections for any portions of the structure not indicated on the drawings shall be completed by the contractor. Such design shall conform to the requirements of the current issue of the Specifications for the Design, Fabrication, and Erection of Structural Steel for Buildings of the American Institute of Steel Construction. These design shop drawings shall be submitted for approval, before any material is fabricated. Subsequent to approval, no modifications shall be made by the contractor."

Questions: 1. Does the specification indicate preferential treatment and restrictions of free competition among suppliers of building materials?

2. Does the specification encourage or suggest the furnishing of free engineering services by the manufacturer of the building materials?

3. Should the consulting engineer do detailing work for contractors (fabricators and material vendors) on the same project for which he is engaged as the consulting engineer?

4. Should the consulting engineer solicit such detailing work on the basis of being the engineering consultant?

5. Should the consulting engineer approve the materials and

shop drawings of the fabricator for the project on which he is engaged as the consulting engineer?

(A.E., June, 1960. p. 38)

3.4 Facts: Consulting engineering firms issue, or cause to be issued by their retained public relations firms, press releases announcing retention of the firm for a particular project. The press releases generally state the nature and scope of the project, the purpose and benefit of the project to the client or the public, and in many instances some factual data about the background and qualification of the firm.

Questions: Does the issuance of press releases by or for the consulting firm constitute advertising of a self-laudatory nature, proscribed by Section 2 of the Canons of Ethics?

(A.E., July, 1960. p. 34)

3.5 Facts: A number of companies which require engineers for the design and development of their products have found it difficult in recent years to recruit a sufficient number of qualified engineers. As one means of contacting engineers interested in their type of work, these companies, individually, maintain temporary recruiting facilities in connection with various industrial exhibitions and meetings of professional and technical societies to interview those engineers in attendance who might be seeking employment, or a change of employment.

In some cases, other companies engaged in similar types of business and requiring engineers with the same type of background and qualification, are fearful of losing their engineers to their competitors and therefore will not allow their engineers to attend exhibitions and meetings where their engineers might be enticed to other employment.

Questions: 1. Is it ethical for a company to maintain recruiting facilities at industrial exhibitions and professional and technical meetings?

2. Is it ethical for an employed engineer to discuss employment with a competitor of his current employer?

3. Is it ethical for an employed engineer to accept employment with a competitor of his current employer?

4. Is it ethical for a company to prohibit their engineers from attending exhibitions and meetings where the engineers might be exposed to other employment offers?

(A.E., Apr., 1961. p. 33)

3.6 Facts: A state sanitary engineer works with communities in promoting adequate sewage and sanitary installations. Some small local communities become interested in the program and desire to construct appropriate facilities. These communities ask the state sanitary engineer for a list of qualified consulting engineers to handle such work. The plans prepared by the consultants will require approval by the state sanitary engineer or his office.

Questions: 1. Should the state sanitary engineer submit a list of qualified consulting engineers?

2. If the answer to question 1 is "yes," should he restrict the list to those firms known personally to him and which he believes to be qualified?

(A.E., May, 1961. p. 34)

3.7 Facts: Engineer "A" has a degree in mechanical engineering and is registered as a professional engineer under the state engineering registration law. He has had 15 years of experience in mechanical engineering work, including $7\frac{1}{2}$ years of mechanical and electrical design of all types of buildings. He has designed the electrical systems for several buildings.

Engineer "B," holder of a degree in electrical engineering and registered as a professional engineer under the state law, filed a complaint with the state professional engineering society alleging that Engineer "A" had acted unethically in designing electrical systems in view of his education and registration based on his proficiency as a mechanical engineer. The complaint does not question the competency of Engineer "A," nor were any plans submitted by Engineer "B" to sustain a charge of lack of quality of the design work of Engineer "A," even though such plans were requested by the state society.

Questions: 1. Is Engineer "A" unethical in practicing electrical engineering when his major field was mechanical engineering?

2. Is Engineer "A" unethical in practicing any branch of engineering other than his major field, provided he is competent to do so?

3. Is Engineer "B" required to show by exhibits that Engineer "A" is incompetent?

(*A.E.*, June, 1961. p. 34)

3.8 Facts: A consulting engineering firm was retained by a city to design street pavement, the client requesting that the firm design for alternate bids based on asphalt and concrete. The alternate designs were to be for equal quality and service.

When bids were submitted it was found that the one design (A) was approximately 15 per cent above the other design. (B) The city rejected all bids and called for new bids on a revised design for (A). On the new design the (A) standards were lowered, but the (B) design was not changed.

At the second bid letting, the new (B) bids were all lower than the revised (A) bids by about 7 per cent. The consulting firm recommended the award for the revised (A) design.

Question: 1. Is it consistent with the Canons of Ethics for a professional engineer to comply with a client's request for a reduction in standards or quality in order to lower the price on a particular material?

2. Was it ethical for the engineer to recommend the award of a contract based on a design of lower standards at a higher price?

(*A.E.*, July, 1961. p. 47)

3.9 Facts: A municipality selected three engineering firms for interview on the design of a certain water and sewage plant. Each firm proposed virtually the same fee, based on the recommended fee schedule of the state society of professional engineers. The city officials asked each firm to state a figure of the amount of reduction from the fee which it would grant, based on the fact that the city would furnish the preliminary engineering report, partial estimates during construction, all inspectors and resident engineers and other data of value to the engineers in performing their work.

The three firms discussed the request jointly and agreed on a uniform credit of $10,000 for the data and services to be furnished by the city. The engineering firms considered that an agreement among them was necessary in order to prevent the procedure from being converted from one of negotiation to one of competitive bidding, it appearing that the city would grant the contract to the firm offering the highest credit.

Questions: 1. Would it have constituted competitive bidding for the several engineers to offer independently the city a reduction in the fee?

2. Was it unethical for the firms involved to confer and agree on a standard credit figure to be offered to the city?

(A.E., August, 1961. p. 40)

3.10 Facts: The following situations are consolidated into one case because they involve the same ethical principles:

Situation "A"—A Consulting engineer who has done considerable work for a public body makes it a practice to take certain staff engineering employees of the agency to lunch or dinner three or four times a year, at an average cost of $5 per person. He also makes it a practice to give certain members of the engineering staff Christmas presents at an average cost of $10 each.

Situation "B"—Certain engineering employees of an industrial firm, who are in a position to recommend for or against the purchase of products used by the company, regularly receive cash gifts ranging from $25 to $100 from salesmen for particular products.

Situation "C"—Upon completion of a major engineering contract held by a consulting engineer, the chief engineer of the client who worked directly and intimately with the consultant receives a new automobile of the value of approximately $4,000 from the consultant with a letter stating that the gift is in appreciation of his close and friendly cooperation and assistance in the successful performance of the work.

Questions: 1. Was it ethical for the engineers in the above instances to offer any of the gifts to the employees?

2. Was it ethical for the engineers in the above instances to accept any of the gifts tendered them?

(*A.E.*, September, 1961. p. 45)

3.11 Facts: Engineering firms "A," "B," and "C" are separately invited by a client to appear at an interview to discuss various aspects of an engineering design project which the client has under consideration. Each invitation makes it clear that the interview will be of a preliminary nature, following which the firm may be selected for the project. At the separate interviews, unknown to each other, each firm is asked to submit in writing a detailed proposal of the scope of the services to be furnished, including a statement of the estimated charges for engineering services, expressed in terms of money, man hours, or other work units. Prior to submitting such a proposal, each firm learns that the others have also been asked to furnish similar information.

Questions: 1. Would it be proper for the firms, acting independently, to provide the client with a statement of the estimated charges for engineering services expressed in terms of money, man hours, or other work unit information?

2. On learning of the full facts, were the engineering firms obligated to decline to participate further?

(*A.E.*, October, 1961. p. 38)

3.12 Facts: A registered engineer, as a candidate for election to a public office, was the subject of a political advertisement containing his photograph and a reproduction of his professional engineer's seal. The paid political advertisement was as follows:

"Vote for John Doe—We need an engineer on the Port Commission! That's simple common sense, isn't it? John Doe is an experienced licensed engineer with years of rich accomplishments. He is a builder who disdains delay. He acts now! Sound in decision. As an engineer, he stands highly regarded in wide areas.

"John Doe has effectively performed his engineering skills here at home as the elected ———— County Engineer, in the building of the famed Alcan Highway into Alaska and on important projects in Latin America.

"As an elected public administrator he has served on the board of ――― Commissioners in highly creditable manner and also as an elected member of the State Legislature. And today is serving in stellar manner as an elected member of the ――― City Council, where his wisdom and judgment have stood out in behalf of the people. Doe has earned the public's positive confidence.

"The ――― Port Commission has long needed an engineer as one of its members. John Doe is that man!

"We need an Engineer on our Board of Port Commissioners. (Paid Political Advertisement.)"

(Note: Also shown on the advertisement were a photograph of the candidate and a reproduction of the PE seal.)

Questions: 1. Is the text of the advertisement unethical?

2. Is this an appropriate use of the seal?

(*A.E.*, November, 1961. p. 34)

3.13 Facts: Two individuals, "A" and "B," neither of whom is a registered professional engineer, are in the process of forming a firm (partnership) to engage in engineering work (consulting, surveying, and estimating). One of these men, "A," is a graduate engineer who has been in the construction field for many years. "A" and "B" obtain a job and engage the services of two registered engineers, "X" and "Y," to perform and certify certain phases of the work connected with this particular job.

"X" and "Y" are full-time staff members of a state university and engage in outside work of this nature only on a spare-time basis. "A" and "B" explain their situation to "X" and "Y" and tell them that as soon as the firm is established another registered engineer, "Z," is to be employed on a full-time basis and that "X" and "Y's" services would be required only until that time.

During this interim period, "A" and "B" complete the legal requirements for the formulation of their partnership, the firm is established, an office rented, and cards printed advertising the firm as engaging in civil engineering, surveying, and estimating work.

"Z" for some reason does not go to work for the newly formed company and "X" and "Y" are the only registered engineers connected with the firm. Their employment, however, is still on a part-time basis and since they both live and work in a city some distance from the firm's place of business, they can exercise no immediate control or direction over the practices and work done by the other members of the engineering company.

According to the applicable state law, if a firm engages in the practice of professional engineering in the state at least one member or employee of the firm must be a registered professional engineer and all work done by the firm shall be carried on under his immediate responsible direction.

Question: With the situation stated above, what is the ethical position of "X" and "Y"?

(A.E., January, 1962. p. 35)

3.14 Facts: Engineer "A" has applied for an engineering position, has been interviewed and has been advised by the prospective employer that his application is being favorably considered. However, he has not been employed and no commitment has been made to him. Engineer "B" learns of the opening and, knowing that Engineer "A" is under favorable consideration, applies to the employer for the same position. In presenting his qualifications, Engineer "B" does not refer to Engineer "A" in any way. Engineer "A" learns of Engineer "B's" action and alleges that he acted unethically in applying for the position knowing that he (Engineer "A") was under favorable consideration.

Question: Did Engineer "B" act unethically in applying for a position knowing that another engineer was being favorably considered for the same position at that time?

(A.E., April, 1962. p. 41)

3.15 Facts: A state association of members of local school boards provides for displays at their annual convention. The exhibits are primarily taken by producers and distributors of products and materials which are used in the construction or operation of the schools. Engineering and architectural firms in the state have been invited to participate in such exhibits, paying for the exhibit space and providing their own material for the displays and personnel to explain their services to those attending the convention.

Question: Is it ethical for an engineer in private practice to participate in the exhibit and prepare and staff a booth explaining his services and qualifications for possible use by school authorities?

(A.E., June, 1962. p. 36)

3:16 Facts: An engineer employed by the ABC Company is assigned by his supervisor to develop processing equipment for the manufacture of certain chemical products. In his previous employment with the XYZ Company, the engineer had participated in the development of similar equipment. The technical information concerning the equipment has not been published in the technical press, or otherwise released. By virtue of his previous involvement in its development, the engineer is familiar with the equipment and the principles of its design. His superiors in the ABC Company suggest that this knowledge will be useful in developing similar equipment for their use and expect him to make his knowledge concerning the particular equipment available to the ABC Company to aid in the development of the similar equipment.

Question: May the engineer ethically apply his knowledge to the development of equipment for his employer based on experience and information gained in similar work for a previous employer, without the consent of the latter?

(A.E., July, 1962. p. 33)

3.17 Facts: A manufacturing company holds a contract for the development and production of a completely automated mass transportation system. A failure of the system, should it occur, would endanger the public safety. Periodic engineering tests have been conducted of the various components during the development period, but the assembly fails the final tests. The engineer who is manager of the department charged with responsibility for the project reports the failure to his superiors. He is told, however, that in order to meet contract commitments the equipment will be shipped to the client without notifying the client of the failure of the final tests. The engineer voices objection to this decision, but learns that the shipment subsequently is made to the client.

Question: Does the engineer have any further ethical duty in these circumstances?

(*A.E.*, August, 1962. p. 32)

3.18 Facts: For many years the ABC Company has manufactured a product which enjoys a high quality rating in the industry and among the public. Competing manufacturers have now introduced a similar product of lower quality at lower cost, and this competition has caused a serious decline in the sales of the product manufactured by the ABC Company. To meet this competition, the ABC Company instructs its engineers to redesign its product in order that it may be made available to the market at lower cost. Upon receiving these instructions, some of the engineers question whether such an action would be consistent with the Canons of Ethics because a lower quality product under the same brand name would mislead the public into accepting a product of lesser quality in the mistaken belief that it meets the high quality standards with which the product has been associated in the public mind for many years.

Question: Do the engineers have a proper interest and ethical obligation to protest the company's decision, or to refuse to design a lower quality product?

(*A.E.*, September, 1962. p. 47)

3.19 Facts: Engineer "A" is retained by a municipality to prepare an engineering design. Engineer "B," an employee of the same municipality, is directed by the municipality to check the design before Engineer "A's" contract is completed. Engineer "B" advised Engineer "A" that he had been assigned the task of reviewing and commenting on Engineer "A's" design. Engineer "B" does not agree with certain features in Engineer "A's" plans and specifications and reports the areas of disagreement to his employer and to Engineer "A."

Question: Is it ethical for Engineer "B" to review the plans and specifications drawn by Engineer "A" and to point out to his employer the area of disagreement?

(*A.E.*, October, 1962. p. 37)

3.20 Facts: Professional engineers often own, manage, or work in organizations which engage primarily in research and development. In recent years there has been a substantial increase in this type of engineering or scientific activity. The normal procedure for securing contracts for research and development projects from Federal agencies (which constitutes a major part of R&D work) includes the following steps:

a) The government agency advertises a need for a study of a particular technical problem.

b) Interested firms reply, setting forth their capability for the work, including experience, equipment, personnel and financial condition.

c) On the basis of these replies the agency invites one or more of the firms deemed to be qualified to submit a proposal, based on the government's statement of the work.

d) The R&D firm presents a technical proposal and a financial proposal, including a breakdown of estimated costs covering such items as labor, overhead, materials, and travel. More than one firm may be invited to submit information and a proposal during this stage.

e) Agency officials may hold conferences with officials of the firm or firms to further evaluate the technical and financial aspects of the proposal. The agency then makes its selection of the firm and negotiates a contract. Generally, the financial arrangement establishes the items of cost which are allowable and stipulates a fixed fee for profit of the firm.

Question: Is it ethical for engineers competitively to negotiate R&D contracts under the procedure outlined?

(*A.E.*, December, 1962. p. 32)

3.21 Facts: An engineering consultant has been retained by a County Metropolitan Commission to perform all necessary engineering and advisory services. The Commission does not have an engineering staff, so the consultant acts as the staff for the Commission in the preparation of sewerage and water studies, the establishment and financing of sanitary districts, and reviews and approves plans submitted by other engineers.

The same consultant has also been retained by a private company to perform the engineering design for a development of several thousand housing units. Involved are extensive contract negotiations between the Commission and the developer for the construction and financing of sanitary and water facilities for the development. As consultant to the Commission, the engineer will under the circumstances have a key role in the negotiations.

Question: Does the dual role of the engineer constitute a conflict of interest?

(A.E., January, 1963. p. 36)

3.22 Facts: The ABC Company has for many years been a client of Consulting Engineer "A" and this is generally and widely known in the community among engineers. Consulting Engineer "B" contacts the ABC Company, offers his services, describes his organization and its experience, and leaves a brochure with a company official. His contract and offer of service are of a general nature and not in connection with any specific pending project.

Question: Was it ethical for Engineer "B" to contact the ABC Company knowing of the relationship between the company and Engineer "A"?

(A.E., March, 1963. p. 48)

The group of assignments below are reprinted, (with permission) from a Forum on Professional Relations published in various issues of *Civil Engineering.* The Forum consisted of hypothetical questions and answers presented by Dr. Daniel W. Mead, a Past President of the American Society of Civil Engineers. The published answers to these questions may be found in the issue of *Civil Engineering (C.E.)* indicated at the end of each question.

3.23 Should an engineer or inspector accept minor favors, common among friends, from a contractor or superintendent of construction, such as cigars, theater tickets, and so forth?

(C.E., Sept., 1942. p. 526)

3.24 A senior engineering student had signed up with a company of good standing about three months before graduation. After spending considerable time in obtaining further information concerning the work available and the general nature of the particular job he had accepted, he found that the thing he would like best to do was not offered by this company. Would he be justified in asking for a release? Must he take this first job if he is positive that he is making a mistake? What would be the best thing to do in a case like this?

(*C.E.*, Nov., 1942. p. 628)

3.25 An engineer supervising the work on a project is able to suggest to the contractor many money-saving methods that do not lower the quality of the work. While on the job the engineer eats at the contractor's mess house. Should he accept his board from the appreciative contractor?

(*C.E.*, Dec., 1942. p. 691)

3.26 A sales engineer is sent out to determine the needs of a certain installation for a prospective customer. He finds that a definite type is required and knows that the only machine, similar to the desired type, manufactured by his firm is not correctly applicable and will probably make the installation unsatisfactory, and there is not time enough to design a special machine. However, he also knows a competitor whose machine would exactly fill all requirements. Should the engineer recommend the machine made by his company or the machine manufactured by the competitor? Does the client or his company come first?

(*C.E.*, Jan., 1943. p. 37)

3.27 "A" owned a mining right which he considered valuable but which he was unable to develop on account of lack of capital. "B" was employed by a mining company which was anxious to acquire "A's" rights but pretended indifference, hoping that this would cause "A" to be willing to sell at a low figure. "A" approached "B" and told him that he would give him a certain sum of money if he would persuade his company to buy his rights, for a stated sum. "B" knew that the company would be glad to obtain the rights at this figure. Was "B" justified in accepting a commission from "A"?

(*C.E.*, Feb., 1943. p. 108)

3.28 A young engineer employed by an engineering firm has had extensive experience in virtual charge of a large piece of important work that was being done for one of the firm's clients. Recognizing the fact that he would be of considerable value to the client because of his detailed knowledge of the work under construction, he applied for a position which finally was offered him at a higher salary than that which he was receiving from the engineering firm. Is he justified in applying for and accepting such a position?

(*C.E.*, Mar., 1943. p. 148)

3.29 In a certain large corporation which employs many men, it is the practice of the superintendent and other officials of the company to have their automobiles overhauled and repaired at the company's repair shop, and to have more or less work done at their homes by the company's men and on the company's time. Should it be considered bad practice if the workmen made small tools and other things for themselves on the company's time and from the company's materials?

(*C.E.*, Apr., 1943. p. 186)

3.30 An engineer who had purchased a number of shares of stock in a local public service company was asked by the directors of the company to make a report on a project which they had under consideration. The directors of the company were ignorant of the fact that the engineer owned stock in the company. Should the engineer accept the job?

(*C.E.*, May, 1943. p. 231)

3.31 A young engineer through carelessness damages a transit which he was using on certain work for the state. The transit was repaired at state expense. The work on which this transit was used was delayed by the action, and the engineer in charge was obliged to make a trip to the state capital in order to secure the repair of the transit. Was the engineer justified in taking $25 offered to him by the young engineer who caused the damage?

(*C.E.*, June, 1943. p. 287)

3.32 The purchasing agent for a large concern purchases a large number of trucks annually. One particular kind of truck has been very satisfactory and is very popular with the purchasing agent. The makers of this truck also makes a pleasure car which the purchasing agent is thinking of buying. When he goes to purchase the car, he finds that the dealer, who is also the dealer from whom he buys the trucks, is willing to sell him the pleasure car at a price a great deal lower than at which the car is ordinarily sold. Should he buy the car at the price offered?

(*C.E.*, July, 1943. p. 329)

3.33   The chief designing engineer of a large company receives an urgent call from the chief engineer of another company, asking if he knows where an engineer can be found who would be qualified to do a certain type of work and who would be willing to work for $4,000 a year, the position being permanent. The only qualified person known to the chief designing engineer is a member of his own staff whose salary is $2,500 per year, who is regularly employed but not under contract for any specific period. The chief designing engineer replies that he knows of no qualified person, and does not mention the opening to the engineer on his staff for important work would be seriously retarded if he lost the man in question. Has he acted fairly and ethically?

(*C.E.*, Aug., 1943. p. 392)

3.34   A friend of Engineer "A," out of work and in need of employment, applied for a job in "B's" office, for which he was very poorly fitted. However, because of his fine personality he was being earnestly considered for the work. The job involved considerable responsibility and the young engineer lacking this experience would, in "A's" opinion, need time to work successfully into the position. The applicant referred to "A" and the company has asked "A" to give his opinion of the man and his ability for the position for which he has applied. Should "A," with his knowledge of this applicant, advise the company concerning his real opinion of the man's qualifications for the job, or should he so word his letter as to retain the friendship of the young engineer and let the company find for itself from experience the true worth of the young man seeking employment?

(*C.E.*, Oct., 1943. p. 498)

3.35 An engineer in general practice was retained by a client to prepare plans, estimates, and specifications, and to inspect and superintend the construction of certain works. In this capacity the engineer became the interpreter and arbiter of the contract and specifications. The contractor who had taken the contract, realizing the experience and ability of the engineer in his specialty, desired to employ him at the same time on another project of a similar nature which he had in view. The engineer had ample time for both jobs. Should he have accepted or rejected the contractor's offer?

(C.E., Dec., 1943. p. 590)

3.36 An engineer makes plans and writes specifications for an installation that is somewhat novel and unique. Is he justified in using essentially these same plans a second time, if no stipulation to the contrary has been made by the client for whom the first work was done and if no data supplied by the first client are used?

(C.E., Dec., 1943. p. 590)

3.37 An engineer in charge of design and construction of a large plant feels that his employers do not correctly interpret his contract with reference to compensation, and they refuse to pay what he thinks are his just dues under the contract. He enters into an agreement with his employers' contractor to pad the quantities. This results in the contractor's receiving overpayments, which extra sum he turns over to the engineer as compensation. What is the ethics of this situation?

(C.E., Jan., 1944. p. 26)

3.38 A municipal board which had no capable engineer in its employ hired a firm of consulting engineers to prepare designs, receive bids, and recommend the award for a bridge. The engineer of the company, who received the contract on a pound basis, prepared an alternate plan for a structure of better appearance, of equal strength, and fully in accord with the specifications but 8% less in weight. The bridge company's engineer submitted his alternate plan to the consulting firm who turned it down as being likely to injure their reputation, and the alternate design was buried in their files. What else could the fabricating company's engineer do?

Was the submission of an alternate design of the bridge by the contractor's engineer, after bids had been taken, the proper procedure for the contractor? If so, should the engineer of the bridge company make further attempts to secure the adoption of what he considers a more satisfactory and economical design?

(C.E., Mar., 1944. p. 119)

3.39   A consulting engineer is employed by a municipality to examine the safety of the design of a municipal structure, which is to be built from plans from another consulting engineering firm. During his examination it becomes quite clear that the construction cost will be high, that the annual operating expense, including maintenance and depreciation, will be exorbitant, and that there will be a large waste of public funds. What obligation, if any, does the consulting engineer have in the matter of reporting this to the municipal authorities?

(C.E., Apr., 1944. p. 168)

3.40   An engineer is making plans and specifications for a sewer system. Is it ethical for him to be financially interested in a concern manufacturing an article that may be used under the specifications, such as sewer pipe?

(C.E., June, 1944. p. 264)

3.41   A junior engineer not yet middle-aged has, as a result of some years of unsuccessful practice, been obliged to accept a position as draftsman in a large engineering firm and at a loss in salary. He has been promised advancement, but finds that invariably those who receive such advancement are agreeable fellows, whereas his temperament is such that he is kept in the position of draftsman at a salary hardly sufficient to meet the expenses of a growing family. How can he overcome this condition, which is discouraging and embittering him?

(C.E., July, 1944. p. 304)

3.42   A young engineer, "A," is employed by a certain firm and is—by verbal agreement—to remain with the company for two years. At the end of the first year, he is approached by another firm which desires to employ him. "A" does not mention his agreement with the first firm but suggests a salary which he considers so exhorbitant that it would not be considered. The new firm, however, is satisfied with the salary mentioned and agrees to it if the young engineer will immediately undertake the work. What should the young engineer do?

(*C.E.*, Aug., 1944. p. 363)

3.43 A young engineer accepts a position with a practicing engineer whom he does not know very well. After a short time he discovers that his employer is dishonest, although he has never asked the young engineer to engage in any crooked action himself. Should the young engineer retain his job?

(*C.E.*, Sept., 1944. p. 404)

3.44 A municipality hires the services of an engineer on a salary basis of $3,000 per year. Is the engineer justified in doing private work during his spare time and keeping the pay therefrom for his own private use?

(*C.E.*, Oct., 1944. p. 444)

3.45 An engineer employed by a power company, upon examining the plant of a subscriber, becomes aware that the subscriber can save money by making certain changes in certain apparatus in use. Should he inform the subscriber or the power company for which he is working of this fact?

(*C.E.*, Nov., 1944. p. 478)

3.46 An engineering student who expected to graduate in June received in March an offer for a position from Company *A*. This he immediately accepted with the understanding that he was to begin work on July 1. In May, the student received from Company *B* an offer which he liked much better and which he thought offered a better chance for advancement. The student had signed no formal contract with Company *A*. What should he do?

(*C.E.*, Dec., 1944. p. 525)

3.47 Bids for some paving were received by the city council in a small city. Among these was a bid from a contractor, who was a personal friend of many of the aldermen. The contractor's bid was as low as any other presented. Is the council warranted in awarding the work to this contractor, if it is satisfied with his experience along the line in question?

(C.E., Jan., 1945. p. 33)

3.48　A member of a St. Louis (Mo.) consulting firm was recommended by friends to an out-of-the-way municipality in lower Louisiana, to provide plans and specifications for, and superintend the construction of, a water works plant. The consulting engineer, learning that the officials and citizens of this municipality had no experience in employing consulting engineers, entered into an agreement to do the work for them without any stipulated price. Later, he sent them a bill for his services at a rate 50% higher than he would have asked for the same services in Illinois. What is the ethics in the case?

(C.E., Feb., 1945. p. 96)

3.49　An engineer was employed to design and supervise the construction of a plant. While the construction was in progress he made suggestions to the contractor regarding the methods employed, with the result that the contractor received a larger profit. After final payments had been made to the contractor and engineer, the contractor offered the engineer a reward for his suggestions. Should the engineer accept or reject?

(C.E., Mar., 1945. p. 149)

3.50　A young man is in the employ of an engineering concern, which is supervising the work being done by an honest and reliable firm of contractors. The contractors, having had an opportunity to observe the young man on the job and to see that he is very capable, offer him a position in their organization at the same salary he is getting from the engineering concern. If the young man feels that he is bettering himself and gives his employer sufficient notice, is he justified in taking the new position while the engineering firm and the contractor still have business relations with each other?

(C.E., June, 1945. p. 287)

3.51 A large firm of consulting engineers opened a branch office in a smaller town, where much future work was being contemplated, and they placed one of the junior members of the firm in charge. In the course of two years the new business, growing out of the construction of a new sanitary sewer and water system, was given to the engineering firm without competition. However, when a large $800,000 paving project came up, an outside firm specializing in paving came in and, at the proper time, underbid the local firm and completely convinced the town of its superior ability to do the work. The local firm had, without solicitation, made many preliminary surveys, plans, and estimates in the hope of getting the work in question. This firm did not specialize in paving, but had made a fine record doing some difficult paving in towns located in the mountains.

Granting that the firm specializing in paving was better equipped to handle the job, was it ethical for it to come into the town where the other firm had established itself and gone to no little expense and effort to make a good record?

(*C.E.*, July, 1945. p. 330)

3.52 A young engineer working for a large manufacturing company has an opportunity to do some work outside his regular hours with the company. The work is not technical and is in no way connected with the company. Is the engineer justified in employing his spare time in such work?

(*C.E.*, Aug., 1945. p. 381)

3.53 An undergraduate, who attended the University of Wisconsin, in the chemical engineering department, for three years, worked one year in the chemical department of a medium-sized industrial concern. His work consisted in supervising a chemical process which was secret. The young man left and finished his university training. Near the end of his last year, a very attractive offer was made to him by a person who did not know these facts. The offer was for a position in a large industrial plant. Is the young man violating professional ethics if he accepts the position?

(*C.E.*, Sept., 1945. p. 433)

3.54 A university student, enrolled in the electrical engineering course, is offered part-time employment with one of the telephone companies associated with the A-system about a year before the time for him to graduate. The representative of the company tells the student that the company intends to help him through school by giving him employment during the following school year on a telegraph repeater maintenance job, and that after graduation it plans to put him in the engineering office as a repeater man. The work given him while in school is light and involves easy hours, and he gets well paid for doing it as it is of a special nature. He is benefited, and the A-company also receives full value for the service he has given while holding the job. After the student graduates and goes through the company's special six-weeks course in order to learn more about the repeater work, he is offered a good position with rather unusual opportunities in another company. Should he accept, or what would he do in this case?

(C.E., Oct., 1945. p. 481)

3.55 If an inspector on a job saved a contractor considerable money by showing him an easier method or short cut in doing some work, would the inspector be justified in receiving remuneration in money or otherwise from the contractor?

(C.E., Nov., 1945. p. 519)

3.56 A few years ago a student was working on an engineering crew, which had charge of a grade-separation project. Occasionally the contractor would send a box of cigars and a carton of cigarettes over to the office. These were accepted. Did the crew violate any ethical consideration?

(C.E., Dec., 1945. p. 566)

Additional Problems in Ethics:

3.57 A senior engineering student receives invitations to visit two different companies for job interviews on successive days, both companies being located in the same distant city. Both companies send checks to cover all expenses for the trip, including round-trip plane fare. Should the student accept both checks?

3.58 A senior engineering student receives an invitation to visit a company in his home town for a job interview, during the Christmas holiday period. The student intended to return home for the holidays, regardless of any interviews. Should he accept the travel expense from the company?

3.59 A supervisor asks an engineer to change a report on data taken in the field so that the report no longer represents the engineer's estimate of the actual conditions. Should he change the report as requested by the supervisor, who has many more years of experience?

3.60 A supervisor, to whom you are next in line for promotion, has become discourteous, argumentative and made himself rather unavailable to both customers and his subordinates. Should you report this to his superiors, who are unaware of the situation?

3.61 An engineer was dropped from membership in a professional society for nonpayment of dues. Some years later he reapplies for admission indicating that he had not paid his dues because he had been serving a jail sentence for conviction of fraud. Should he be readmitted to the professional society, assuming he is willing to satisfy the requirements for back dues?

3.62 A non-registered engineer prepares, in his spare time, some design drawings for a personal venture. The design requires the seal of a registered engineer. The designer offers a fee to a registered engineer (not his employer) to check and place his seal on the design. Should the registered engineer accept the offer?

3.63 An engineer is asked to serve as an expert witness in a lawsuit against one of his clients. If the lawsuit is unrelated to any work the engineer has performed for his client, should he accept the offer and fee for serving as an expert witness?

3.64 A registered professional engineer is educated and experienced in the field of mechanical engineering. He employs a non-registered electrical engineer, and undertakes consulting work in the areas of electrical engineering in which he believes his employee is competent, but of which he knows very little personally. Is this ethical if registration in this state gives the title, Professional Engineer, without designation of field?

3.65   Is it ethical for an engineer to submit a bid, in competition with others, to manufacture an item or build a project in accordance with a design prepared by him for a client?

3.66   A client retains an engineer to make some additions to a project which had been completed several years ago. The engineer in preparing the design for the additions discovers some mistakes in his original design which lower the factor of safety beyond desirable limits. The engineer can correct his mistakes and make it appear as though the costs for the corrections are a necessary part of the additions. Should he correct the mistakes? Should he inform the client of all the details?

3.67   A contractor encounters some unanticipated costs due to an oversight in the engineering design. The contractor is entitled to reimbursement for these costs and the design engineer (an employee of the owner) would like to see him receive this reimbursement. However, the red tape involved in the project is so complex that the contractor is unlikely to be reimbursed through any straight-forward reporting of the facts. Would it be ethical for the design engineer to report to his company a quantity of work greater than actually performed, in order to reimburse the contractor for the unanticipated complications?

3.68   Is it ethical for an engineer to accept a contingent contract in which he will be paid only if, upon completion of his design, the project proves to be economically feasible and financing can be arranged?

3.69   A young engineer is assigned to show a visiting engineer through his company's plant. The young engineer shows unusual courtesy to the visitor and in appreciation the visitor adds $50 to his expense account and offers to buy the young engineer a gift of his choice. Should the young engineer accept the gift?

BIBLIOGRAPHY

(1) DRINKER, HENRY S. *Legal Ethics*. New York: Columbia University Press, 1953. 448 pp.

(2) HYMAN, D. *It's Still the Law*. New York: David McKay Company, Inc., 1961.

SUGGESTED ADDITIONAL READING

"Ethical Standards and Professional Conduct," *The Annals*, Volume 297. Philadelphia: American Academy of Political and Social Sciences, January, 1955. 199 pp.

"Ethics of the Professions and of Business," *The Annals*, Volume 101. Philadelphia: American Academy of Political and Social Sciences, May, 1922. 315 pp.

CHAPTER 4

The Engineer and Society

4-1. HISTORY OF ENGINEERING. The exact origin of the engineering profession would be difficult to establish. The origin can be considered to have been at the time the first man used his *ingenuity* to adapt the materials and forces of nature to meet his needs. Thus structural engineering may have begun when the first tree was felled across a stream for use as a bridge; sanitary engineering may have begun when the first man diverted a brook to bring drinking water closer to his abode.

Egyptian hieroglyphs, as early as 2800 B.C., record the title "chief of works" for the individual having primary responsibility and duties in the organized undertakings which might be considered a combination of engineering, architecture, and contracting. Almost every form of engineering was known to the civilizations of antiquity including Egypt, China, Persia, Chaldea, Babylon, Assyria, Phoenicia, Etruria, Palestine, Moab, and Peru. They built canals, public water supplies, docks, harbors, lighthouses, bridges, roads and massive structures. They tested the strength of building materials, planned fortifications, designed engines of attack, devised methods of transport of heavy objects and systems of navigation and communication, and were skilled in metallurgy. The writings of Hero, about 200 B.C., describe a reaction steam engine, a two-cylinder force pump, and a heat engine which was operated by the expansive force of heated air and used for opening doors and other light work.

The "chief of works" held a position of power and influence

in most ancient communities. He was the advisor of the king, his ministers, and his generals, and usually held a sacred office in addition to his secular duties. The origin of the title "engineer" is generally considered to have been first indicated about 200 A.D. in the writings of the Latin historian, Tertullian. Tertullian referred to an early battering ram as an *ingenium,* an invention or product of genius which became known as an engine of war. Some 800 to 1000 years later the title *ingeniator* (engineor, engigneur) came to be used frequently to refer to the men who made engines of war and built fortresses.

In the early days engineering was primarily an art and craft; and those entering the field did so by serving a period of apprenticeship under an experienced engineer. Most of the work accomplished was done with a plentiful supply of labor and materials (primarily wood, stone, and brick). If a structure was built 20 or one hundred times stronger than necessary, it caused little concern because of the abundance of both materials and labor. Experience and patient trial and error were the most important teachers of the engineer. Although some rudimentary mathematics (primarily geometry) had been used for such things as land measuring, it was not until the 17th century that there was a rebirth of the science and mathematics which have become the major tools of the modern engineer.

In the nineteenth century an important series of events took place which brought about a radical change in the engineering profession. Carnot brought forth the first real understanding of the theory of the steam engine in 1824; the dynamo and the electric generator were introduced in 1831; the telegraph and the electric lamp were respectively introduced in 1836 and 1880; the Gold Rush of 1849 gave incentive and capital for great advances in mining engineering; Bessemer presented his important improvement in steelmaking in 1856; and reinforced concrete was introduced in 1868. These made feasible the use of wonderful new materials and equipment which were no longer in the plentiful category of wood, stone, brick, and human and animal labor. The new materials and equipment emphasized the need for efficiency and economy of design and led to a rapidly increasing dependence of the engineering profession on the body of knowledge in mathematics and science, to supplement art and craft.

At this same time the American West was undergoing a rapid expansion. There were not nearly enough experienced engineers to train the large number of apprentice engineers needed to keep up with the swift growth of the American frontier areas. Collegiate training was initiated to attempt both to prepare the many young engineers needed for the frontier and to bring about a greater awareness of the potential applications of mathematics and science. The early graduates of these new engineering schools faced considerable ridicule from the "practical" engineers. The infusion of science and mathematics into the art and craft of engineering, however, could no longer be delayed. At the close of the Civil War there were only four engineering schools in the United States; but within the next thirty years the number increased to 89.

The first organization of the engineering profession is generally considered also to have taken place in relatively recent times. Most of the early engineering works were done under the jurisdiction of the military. Vauban, the famous builder of fortresses for Louis XIV, initiated the idea which resulted in the engineers of the French Army forming an organized group, the Corps du Génie, in 1672. In 1716 a French national highway department, the famous Corps des Ponts et Chaussées, was formed to create an organization of engineers in civil life which paralleled the Corps du Génie of the Army. The parent organization of civilian engineers, in all walks of life, was the Institution of Civil Engineers founded in England in 1818. Some years later the number of civilian engineers who were primarily interested in steam engines and other mechanical devices became large enough to form a separate organization in 1847 called the Institution of Mechanical Engineers. The first five engineering societies (called the Founder Societies) in the United States were the American Society of Civil Engineers (1852), American Institute of Mining, Metallurgical and Petroleum Engineers (1871), American Society of Mechanical Engineers (1880), Institute of Electrical and Electronic

Engineers (1884), and the American Institute of Chemical Engineers (1908). The Founder Societies have been joined by the National Council of State Boards of Engineering Examiners, American Society for Engineering Education, American Institute of Aeronautics and Astronautics, and the Engineering Institute of Canada to form the Engineer's Council for Professional Development (E.C.P.D.) which accredits the various engineering curricula presently offered. The rapid advance of technology has brought forth many additional societies to make a total of almost 100 national technical and professional organizations of potential interest to engineers (see § 4-6). Efforts have been continued through the years, as yet without adequate success, to develop a single organization or voice which could speak for the entire profession in all related matters. The establishment of this unity organization, or unified organizational structure, is one of the major challenges which lies ahead of the engineering profession in its own future development.

4-2. PROFESSIONALISM AND THE FUTURE OF ENGINEERING.

The Engineer's Council for Professional Development has stated the attributes of a profession and of a professional practitioner as follows:

Of a Profession:
1. It must satisfy an indispensable and beneficial social need.
2. Its work must require the exercise of discretion and judgment and not be subject to standardization.
3. It is a type of activity conducted upon a high intellectual plane.
   a) Its knowledge and skills are not common possessions of the general public; they are the results of tested research and experience and are acquired through a special discipline of education and practice.
   b) Engineering requires a body of distinctive knowledge (science) and art (skill). [sic]
4. It must have group consciousness for the promotion of technical knowledge and professional ideals and for rendering social services.
5. It should have legal status and must require well-formulated standards of admission.

Of Professional Practitioners:

1. They must have a service motive, sharing their advances in knowledge, guarding their professional integrity and ideals, and tendering gratuitous public service in addition to that engaged by clients.
2. They must recognize their obligations to society and to other practitioners by living up to established and accepted codes of conduct.
3. They must assume relations of confidence and accept individual responsibility.
4. They should be members of professional groups and they should carry their part of the responsibility of advancing professional knowledge, ideals, and practice.

Primary concepts amongst the above list of attributes of a profession are the necessity for discretion and judgment and the obligation to satisfy beneficial social needs. The professional man cannot be satisfied with the mere physical accomplishment of a task; he must also assume responsibility for the results of his efforts. The professional man cannot be satisfied with the mere learning and use of facts and skills (training); he must also understand the relations between the aims and values associated with his knowledge. To be well-informed is not necessarily to be educated. A man may know how to heat, cool, stress, electrify, and explode; but he is not a professional unless he also knows why he should do it, when he should do it, and for whom he should do it. Having accomplished a task, the professional has the additional obligations to tell others what he has done, why he has done it, and most importantly what further should be done. The public grants to a profession, through legal registration (see § 4-5), more or less tangible monopolies and self governing privileges for which in return the profession is expected to admit to its membership only those with proven competence and trustworthiness.

Theodore Von Karman has stated very succinctly the difference between the professions of the engineer and the scientist: "The scientist explores what is, the engineer creates what had not been." It might also be stated: "The scientist seeks, the engineer does." These statements point out that the major function of the engineer is not the mere studying, but getting things done which need doing; and the engineer should be intent on the doing with less concern on who gets the credit or how much the compensation. A maxim to guide these efforts is: *whatever you do, do it right.* Anxiety to please or to gain additional compensation can cause one to undertake more than there is time to do without rushing and inviting careless mistakes or oversights. One should also recognize that assignments may be offered for which you do not have adequate knowledge or experience, and unless more experienced engineers can be consulted or prior tests or experiments run, the work should not be undertaken. It takes only one serious failure to destroy a career built over a lifetime. Herbert Hoover has expressed very well the extent of the responsibility and liability of the engineer for his work:

"The great liability of the engineer compared to men of other professions is that his works are out in the open where all can see them. His acts, step by step, are in hard substance. He cannot bury his mistakes in the grave like the doctors. He cannot argue them into thin air or blame the judge like the lawyers. He cannot, like the architects, cover his failures with trees and vines. He cannot, like the politicians, screen his shortcomings by blaming his opponents and hope the people will forget. The engineer simply cannot deny he did it. If his works do not work, he is damned. . . . On the other hand, unlike the doctor, his is not a life among the weak. Unlike the soldier, destruction is not his purpose. Unlike the lawyer, quarrels are not his daily bread. To the engineer falls the job of clothing the bare bones of science with life, comfort and hope. No doubt as years go by people forget which engineer did it, even if they ever knew. Or some politician put his name on it. Or they credit it to some promoter who used other people's money. . . . But the engineer himself looks back at the unending stream of goodness which flows from his successes with satisfactions that few professions may know. And the verdict of his fellow professionals is all the accolade he wants." (1:133)

The future of the engineering profession is a function of the increasing dependence of our society upon science and technology. In 1890 there were 280 production workers for every engineer. Today's complex society requires one engineer to about 50 production workers; and the ratio continues to decrease. Early engineering technology replaced animal and manpower to increase tremendously the production potential. More recent efforts such as automation and computor technology have begun to replace elements of man's "brainpower" to vastly expand the dependence upon technology. For the foreseeable future it appears that the world-wide need for engineers will far exceed the available supply that can be graduated from our existing colleges.

Recognition, prestige, and economic rewards are also advancing in the engineering profession. The engineering graduate has been able to command the highest or among the highest starting salaries of all graduates. More and more we see engineers called upon to fill the major executive positions such as Chairman of the Board, President, and Vice-President of our large corporations. Today it is estimated that more than 40 per cent of industrial management received their basic education in engineering, replacing the lawyer, accountant, and banker in these top industrial posts.

Yet more important than economic reward and prestige, the engineering profession is a self-satisfying, creative, challenging profession that offers the utmost in opportunity for every individual to exercise his vigor, ingenuity, and progressiveness, and to see the tangible results of his efforts. The greatest engineering opportunities are not behind us—they are ahead. We have just begun to pass through the entranceway to engineering achievement. Some of the foreseeable great technological challenges immediately ahead include space exploration, further exploration of the depths of the sea and the earth, solar and nuclear energy advances, changes in crystal structure by atomic radiation, combining of television and telephone, mail scanning and reformulation at the destination, and advances in safety and automatic controls for planes and automobiles.

And yet the truly great challenges are not in the above list. Too much of what we have done and for which we strive has been to improve the standard of living of those who need relatively little. We have often worked and strived for luxuries and tended to ignore the world's great needs. We sorely need to work to overcome the social and political barriers which inhibit the extension of our known technology to the underprivileged masses of the world. For if we do not, the underprivileged masses will continually foment war which will tend to engulf us; or our resources will be depleted as we build up arms for defense. There has been great progress in developing instruments of war; but we need greater progress in developing conditions of peace. There has been great progress in developing communications; but we need greater progress in developing what is being communicated. There has been great progress in increasing the efficiency of man's labor to give a new found leisure; but we need greater progress in showing man how to use his leisure efficiently. Engineering has worked with structural systems, electrical systems, and machine systems; but the truly great challenge lies in working with living systems. The beginnings of these endeavors may be seen in the activities of such fields as bio-medical engineering, environmental engineering, urban and regional planning, and operation's analysis. The potential achievements of engineering in working with living systems offer great hope to usher in the good life for which so many have waited for so long a time.

4-3. SPECIALIZATION IN ENGINEERING FIELDS AND FUNCTIONS. Many a young engineer dreams of some day becoming the world's foremost authority in some area of engineering. This however is not necessarily a great accomplishment, as may be seen by the following example. A young graduate was given as his first job assignment the task of taking initial measurements of the stream flow in one of the many hundreds of canals (Canal #523) which crisscross the Everglades. His task was completed at the end of a week and a report filed and accepted. It could therefore be said that this young man, one week after graduation, was the world's foremost authority on the stream flow in Everglades Canal #523. It is quite easy to become the world's foremost authority if one narrows down the area of endeavor sufficiently. Indeed, each and everyone of us are already the world's foremost authority in many areas such as in the knowledge of our own personal tastes and amount of personal possessions. It should be evident that the renowned specialist or authority in a significant area of endeavor must in fact be rather broadly learned. It is also relatively easy to learn something about everything, but essentially impossible to learn everything about anything.

If one wished to know all there was to know about even a relatively narrow area, it can be demonstrated that one would have to know all there is to know about all matters in the universe. If the young engineer mentioned above wished to know *all* there was to know about the stream flow of Everglades Canal #523, he would have to know all there was to know about fluid mechanics. Fluid mechanics crosses many fields of engineering so that it would therefore soon become necessary to know all of engineering and its bases of mathematics and the physical sciences. The stream flow may also be affected by plant, fish, and animal life and therefore he should know all there is to know about the biological sciences. The Canal is created and used by man so that it becomes necessary to know all there is to know about man and his social, political, economic, philosophical, legal, medical, psychological, and cultural problems. The stream flow is affected by meteorological conditions which are in turn affected by the moon and the sun and therefore he must also know all there is to know about these and of all the planets, and galaxies, and ad infinitum.

The specialist or authority in a field of specialization must be well-versed in many areas. The chief engineer for a major project is generally chosen, not merely because of excellence in his own field, but because of his potential ability to integrate successfully all the fields involved in the project. There is no sharp dividing lines between the various fields of engineering either in the college curriculum or in professional practice. The practicing engineer may face emergencies or novel situations alone, where he must rely on his own fundamental knowledge—here again is where breadth of knowledge is important; why one takes the courses that "I'll never use." The well-educated engineer can work efficiently as a member of a team of engineers from many fields such as civil, electrical, and mechanical engineering, and may upon many occasions end up (very successfully) in a field other than that which was his college major.

Specialization may also take place in one or more of the functions of engineering, or types of work common to all fields of engineering. Here also there is no sharp dividing line between the various functions; and the engineer in one function can perform this function better by having a good understanding of other functions. In considering job opportunities one is likely to be affected positively or negatively, according to his personal qualities and interests, by the assigned function more than by the particular field of engineering assigned in the title of the job. Thus if one had a strong preference or dislike for engineering sales, this preference or dislike for sales would not be likely to be affected greatly by the items sold being classified in different fields such as mechanical or electrical engineering. The various functions of engineering can be clarified by noting their relation to the sequence necessary for the accomplishment of typical engineering projects:

MANAGEMENT—APPRAISAL

The initiation and decision of whether or not an enginering project should be undertaken is the major contribution of the function of management. Management is also responsible for the proper coordination of the other (following) functions during the progress of the work. Management must weigh the availability and cost of materials, equipment, manpower, and financing against the projected income or use value. Appraisals and decisions usually must be made based upon partial data utilizing wide experience and judgment of the highest order to determine feasibility, before many thousands of dollars are wasted on the actual design of a project that cannot be financed or is otherwise impractical. Abilities essential for this function are leadership, broad perception, foresight, imagination, initiative, motivation, flexibility, and a willingness to accept responsibility.

RESEARCH—DEVELOPMENT

Many engineering projects require new materials, facts, principles, or processes before the design can proceed; and engineers in the research and development function are called upon to bring these forth. Qualifications for these functions usually include an outstanding scholastic record, advanced theoretical studies (generally at graduate level), and personal qualities of creativeness, patience, versatility, perseverance, manual dexterity, and the ability to think inductively and intuitively.

ANALYSIS–DESIGN

Analysis and design are processes in which facts and ideas are broken down into comprehensible units and converted into detailed plans and specifications from which efficient, economical finished articles or projects can be produced or constructed. The plans and specifications represent predictions of the applicable theories relative to the performance of the desired product or project. Qualifications for analysis and design include judgment, ingenuity, thoroughness, and a good basic knowledge of engineering theory, practice, and economics.

ESTIMATING

Estimates may include the determination of accurate weights, quantities of material and labor, and costs taken from the design drawings and specifications. Upon the basis of the estimates, economic feasibility is checked and a bid proposal for production or construction may be submitted. If the estimates show excessive costs, the detailed breakdown may be an important basis for redesign. The estimating function carries high responsibility, for the success or failure of a business enterprise in our free economy is very largely dependent upon accurate estimates to obtain the delicate balance between being the low-bidder and making a profit. This function requires an ability to observe details, carefulness, knowledge of production and construction methods and costs, organized record keeping, and application to a recurrent type of calculative work.

PRODUCTION–CONSTRUCTION (OR PREVENTION)

Production involves the marshalling of men, materials, and equipment to obtain large quantities of a product, each of which conforms to the design drawings and specifications. Construction involves the same process but usually relates to only one or a limited number of projects. Engineers performing these functions require diligence, promptness, initiative, and the ability to work with people and under pressure. Construction, particularly, may frequently involve travel and relatively short-term assignments.

TESTING–INSPECTION

After production or during construction the conformance with plans and specifications is determined by tests or inspection. Quality control procedures may be established to meet standards of guaranteed performance. These functions require discretion, patience, manual dexterity, and diplomatic ability to reject without antagonizing.

SALES–SERVICE

Highly complex equipment necessitates detailed knowledge of capabilities and limitations by the engineers performing the functions of sales and service. After installation of the equipment, trouble-shooting and other assistance in proper maintenance and operation may also be a responsibility. The sales-service engineer should be courteous, tactful, self-reliant, sincere, friendly, voluble, and must like working with people.

OPERATION–MAINTENANCE

Complex equipment, plants, utilities, refineries, etc., need to have highly skilled and reliable personnel to maintain efficient, safe, continuous, uniform operation. The engineer in these functions is responsible for procurement of raw materials or supplies, direction of personnel, and planning of preventative maintenance. The function demands ingenuity in meeting with emergencies and the highest sense of responsibility and dependability and in turn usually offers a relatively stable type of employment.

EDUCATION–TRAINING

The function of education is closely related to research, as the discovery of new knowledge can hardly be separated from the imparting of existing knowledge. However, the major task of education involves the development of the ability to reason well upon the basis of readily available knowledge. Training involves the development of the ability to perform a task in a specific manner and is particularly important in industry to indoctrinate new employees and to introduce new processes and techniques. Opportunities exist for teaching in engineering colleges, industrial training programs and in the pre-engineering programs of the rapidly expanding junior colleges. It is most desirable to have prior experience in one of the other functions in order to have an adequate perspective of the profession; and graduate study is essential in the college phase of education. Teaching offers an intellectual, stable, idealistic, and satisfying environment for those with qualifications of patience, fluent expression, desire for knowledge, and an ambition both to work with and to serve humanity.

4-4. EMPLOYMENT PRACTICES. In seeking professional employment it is generally preferable to seek the position which one anticipates will be challenging and satisfying, not necessarily the position which offers the best starting pay. If the work is enjoyable and therefore one exerts the maximum effort, the higher pay will most likely be forthcoming. Enough money is needed for the essentials of food, clothing, and housing—beyond this much of our wants approach the insatiable. No matter how much one is paid, it is easy to feel that it should be more. It is the rare individual who doesn't feel that he is deserving of more money, particularly when he starts making comparisons with the earnings of others considered less competent. The world being as it is, it may be best to resign oneself to always being underpaid —and be happy.

Having chosen a field and a function of engineering, a most commonly encountered further employment decision involves that of choosing between employment in a large or small organization. Both small and large organizations are necessary for a free economy—their relative effectiveness depending upon the location, population served, and types of products or services offered.

Interesting and rewarding careers are available in both large and small organizations. Organizational characteristics which appeal to one person may not appeal to another; and each individual must weigh which are best for his particular abilities, personality and interests. It is unlikely that any important general characteristics can be applied to every large organization, or to every small organization; each organization must be evaluated individually. However, it is believed that there are typical characteristics, as summarized below, which are very likely to be found weighted more heavily, respectively, in favor of the large or small organization.

Employment in public agencies tends to show the same characteristics as those found in the large private corporation. Typical characteristic advantages of employment in a large organization include:

1. Usually there is a better organized means of easing the the transition from college to professional practice, and efficiently familiarizing new employees with the entire organization (e.g., formal orientation and in-service training programs).

2. Greater job security is available in the large organizations, which have the financial resources to keep their employees when the work load eases. A very high percentage of new businesses, which would be predominantly small organizations, go bankrupt or close during the first few years of existence thus increasing the instability of employment in the small organization.

3. Comprehensive fringe benefits are usually available in a large organization. These may include group life and health insurance, liberal vacation and sick leave, provisions for retirement supplementing social security, subsidy of tuition for graduate study often including time off during the regular working hours and leaves of absence, and planned recreation programs sometimes including elaborate country club facilities.

4. Technical advancement and quality of experience may be

furthered by better equipped laboratories, shops, research equipment, and libraries generally available in the large organization. In the tax supported organization, with the profit motive eliminated, high quality of work or service can receive prime consideration.

5. Many different levels of supervisory experience are available, allowing a large variety of combinations of technical work and administrative responsibility and authority.

6. New employees changing their area of residence are more likely to find a community of common interest in the large organization where there may be other graduates from their own college, people from their home town, etc.

Typical characteristic advantages of employment in a small organization include:

1. The engineer in the small organization is more likely to retain his identity and be treated as a professional, and not merely an hourly worker punching a time clock. He is assumed to be able to manage his time as is necessary to accomplish his job; while the large organization will tend to have a regularly scheduled coffee break or monitored rest period. In the small organization there may be from 1 to 3 to an office, and not the large open bull-pen area occupied by hundreds of engineers.

2. The smaller size of projects affords more opportunity for the individual engineer to be aware of the entire job from start to finish. A single person frequently can be responsible for the entire job; whereas the multimillion dollar projects of the large organization require hundreds of engineers each aware only of a minute part of the job. The engineer in the small organization tends to deal directly with other agencies such as legal, sales, purchasing, and production staffs affording a broad experience with high relative status. The engineer in the large organization tends to deal with these other agencies through vast complex channels which often tend to hamstring and dictate against good engineering practice.

3. The small organization tends to seek and to be satisfied only with the superior man. Lacking tax support or the savings brought by mass production, it can survive only by high efficiency and output from each employee. Individual achievement can and must be more effectively nurtured and more readily recognized by the top level administration. More and more small organizations are offering fringe benefits, profit-sharing plans and junior partnerships to reward and retain their outstanding employees. The tendency for empire building (Parkinson's Law) and over-staffing within the large organization conversely may encourage inaction and lack of diligence in work habits, and an assemblage of mediocre employees who ride on the productivity of others. The young engineer placed in this atmosphere, who allows himself to join and form habits of daily coffee breaks which last from 5 to 8 hours, may find it difficult later to retain employment in an organization where productivity is expected.

Some of the greatest opportunities for engineering employment lie in fields and organizations where hitherto little use has been made of engineering talent. This type of organization would not be likely to have any systematic recruitment plan, and the employment opportunity is one that usually has to be sought out.

The initial employment of the young engineering graduate is likely to appear relatively routine and simple when compared to the engineering school where, during a typical week, five or six different instructors were each continually setting forth challenging new assignments. Having only a single job assignment which is followed by other single job assignments involving much repetition of the same processes may thus appear to be a situation where there is no progress, or an arrested progress. It should be recognized that most organizations have to specialize in a specific type of work which then tends to create assignments involving a fair amount of repetitious effort. Also, responsibility for the broader more challenging assignments cannot logically be given until the new employee has first demonstrated adequately that he can handle the relatively simple and routine assignments.

W. J. King in his article "The Unwritten Laws of Engineering" has summarized, in an excellent manner, many of the important factors in employment practices which should be considered by every engineer from the recent graduate to the executive. "The Unwritten Laws of Engineering" are reprinted by permission, from the May, June, and July, 1944 issues of *Mechanical Engineering* and are included in Appendix A.

4-5. ENGINEERING REGISTRATION. Registration laws have originated to protect the public against incompetent and unscrupulous individuals in matters affecting the public welfare and in the safeguarding of life, health, and property. The first U. S. engineering registration law was adopted and put into effect in Wyoming in 1907, the impetus coming from a series of faulty engineering designs of several local dams. The practice of professional engineering is regulated today, by means of laws, in all of the states of the U. S. and in most other countries.

Requirements, practices, and procedures vary in the individual states to conform to local problems and judgment as to the best means of accomplishing the purposes of the registration laws. Typical minimum requirements for engineering registration are: an engineering degree from an approved college, four years of professional experience which qualifies one to be in responsible charge of important engineering works, references by other registered engineers indicating their approval of the applicants competency and character, and the passing of examinations covering the basic theory and practice of engineering. The major variations between the requirements of the individual states are in the number of years of required experience, substitution of experience for education, the extent to which the examinations are mandatory or optional, and in the difficulty and length of examinations. The National Council of State Boards of Engineering Examiners, composed of representatives of the individual state boards, has recommended a Model Law and standards for certification which have done much to improve the individual state laws and ease the barriers of interstate practice. The NCSBEE has established a committee of National Bureau of Engineering Registration; National Bureau Certificates are accepted in many of the states. Reciprocity will most generally be granted if an individual has a high level of experience and has become registered by examination in a state giving comprehensive examinations.

In choosing one's early employment consideration should be given as to whether or not the type of experience received will qualify one for registration. For example, experience in the function of engineering sales is not likely to be acceptable for the minimum experience requirements in most states. Experience in the functions of engineering design or research will usually be given full acceptance. Experience in other functions may not be considered on a year for year equivalent basis; and prior investigation of the State Board's practice is recommended before undertaking employment in certain functions.

Some states grant registration by separate fields or branches of engineering; however, most states register individuals as Professional Engineers, with no branch or field designated. The broad title Professional Engineer is given, even though the registration examinations may be in a specific field, because it is most difficult to draw a sharp dividing line between the practices of the various fields of engineering. It is assumed that each Professional Engineer has sufficient ethics and integrity to limit his practice to those areas in which he is competent to practice. It has generally been difficult to restrict legally the use and misuse of the title "engineer" by locomotive operators, television repair men, plumbers, etc.; however, the title Professional Engineer has been effectively legally reserved for members of the profession who are registered. In order to aid in making the public aware of the meaning of Professional Engineer, the National Society of Professional Engineers has encouraged the use of the initials "P.E." after one's name in the same manner the initials "M.D." are used in the medical profession.

The Professional Engineer is expected to act in an ethical

manner and to display diligence and competence in his work. The law cannot expect perfection of any man; that is, to never make a mistake. However, the Professional Engineer can be held legally responsible, and his registration revoked, if there is evidence of gross negligence, incompetence (e.g., practicing in a field outside of one's area of experience), or misconduct. The relatively few failures among the many thousands of great engineering works speaks well for the education, teamwork, and regulation of the engineering profession.

Exemption clauses in state laws generally do not require engineering registration for practice by the following categories of individuals:

1. Officers and employees of the U. S. government;
2. Elective officers of states, counties, and cities;
3. Employees of registered engineers;
4. Owner's practice involving only his personal property, where the public welfare is not affected;
5. Designers of manufactured products where the manufacturer assumes responsibility for quality.

Because of the large number of engineers employed in exempt categories, only a little more than half of the engineers eligible for licensing are presently registered. However, there has been a tremendous growth in both the number and percentage of engineers who are registered, increasing from about 10,000 in the early 1930's to approximately 300,000 today.

There are many reasons why all eligible engineers should consider becoming registered as soon as possible even though they may presently be employed or considering employment in an exempt category. Among these reasons are:

1. One may at some future time receive a signal offer of employment which requires current registration.
2. More and more organizations are using engineering registration as an outside, impartial means of judging the competency of its employees. Salary advances and promotions are being tied in with registration, thus avoiding the

stagnation that may occur if mere seniority of years of employment is the major factor.

3. Circumstances may permit part-time or full-time consulting work (e.g., registration has been indicated to be necessary for qualification as an expert witness), particularly after retirement. Passing of the registration examinations, after retirement, would be quite difficult for most individuals.

4. Support of the engineering registration laws enhances the stature of the profession. The undergraduate degree is essentially only certification of book learning. Registration is an indication of both this and the acquisition of the necessary experience. Many of the engineering societies are requiring registration for eligibility to attain the highest classification of membership. Registration allows one to enjoy an equality with the highest, and a feeling of truly belonging in the profession.

5. Registration gives one an importance and status as a professional in one's general community, not the status of a mere employee.

6. Aspiration for the early completion of registration examinations furnishes incentive for study and self-development. The broad subject matter coverage of the examinations will be easier to cope with, as soon as one is eligible to take the examinations, because the material is relatively fresh in mind. If one waits, he may also find both the examinations and the requirements for registration becoming more difficult each year (e.g., some have suggested that the Master's degree should become the minimum educational requirement for registration).

The first basic theory part of the registration examination may generally be taken just before or shortly after completion of work for the Bachelor's degree in engineering. This part of the examination usually also may be taken on or near the campus, thus avoiding having, after employment, to take time off work and possibly distant travel to a city where the examination is offered. Passing of this basic theory part of the examination gives one registration as an "engineer-in-training," and makes one eligible for this class of membership in the National Society of Professional Engineers. After completion of the required years of experience one may take the remaining portion of the registration examination. Copies of previous examinations will usually be sent to the applicant, by the State Board, for reference in studying. Some of the State Professional Engineering Societies, including Illinois, Missouri, and Pennsylvania, have available for purchase printed refresher courses and/or collections of sample questions. Many local engineering society chapters also periodically sponsor formal refresher courses for those preparing for the registration examinations.

4-6. PROFESSIONAL SOCIETIES. No man can live alone effectively in either his personal or professional life. We all have obligations towards others and in turn can receive many benefits from others. Many engineers rationalize their not joining or participating in professional societies, particularly at the local level, because "they" don't do anything and are not worth the time and expense. What a professional society does is up to its members; and if each member looks for "they" to do everything, obviously nothing will be done. It is quite likely that every professional society would be happy to have such complainants volunteer to do what the complainants believe "they" should do.

Some of the things which professional societies, at national, state and local level can do for the individual, and which the individual can do for the societies, are listed below:

a) The major share of the financial support of professional societies is used to develop, preserve, and disseminate professional knowledge. The society publications and technical papers presented at society meetings are a primary source for the knowledge required to keep up with the advances in enginering technology.

b) The Engineering Societies Library at the United Engineering Center in New York offers availability of its vast storehouse of knowledge to its members through personal visit or by mail. Many engineering schools also offer free privileges of their libraries to members of recognized engineering societies. Today's exploding technology makes every engineer dependent upon access to this information, the accumulation of which is beyond the resources of the individual.

c) The professional society meeting affords less formal contacts with one's peers and superiors than is likely to be found in the daily work environment. Informal discussions at these society meetings gives a place for developing lifelong friendships and for presenting one's problems and ideas to the test, particularly for the young engineer. In school the choices and decisions are relatively simple and the risks relatively minor (e.g., the risk of a lower grade on the examination paper.) In professional practice every day may bristle with important decisions and major risks involving both human lives and economic substance. Too many engineers are afraid to discuss their decisions with others because of apprehension that they may find that a better decision could have been made, or that they may show their weaknesses and ignorance. At least the young engineer should feel free to ask as he is understood to be in a position of the apprentice, an engineer-in-training—even if the more experienced engineers fear to hazard displaying the unenlightenment all of us have.

d) Engineering societies, through the Engineers Council for Professional Development (E.C.P.D.), engage in the accrediting of engineering curricula to furnish both guidance and incentive for the improvement of the standards of professional education.

e) Student chapters of the professional societies afford the beginnings, in universities and colleges, of professional associations and concepts. Sponsored engineering clubs in the high schools offer guidance and motivation towards careers in the profession.

f) The professional societies, through group action, are able to exert a relatively powerful force to protect both the public and members of the profession. This has been done primarily by means of the registration laws, by influencing other national and local legislation, and by the maintenance of the ethical standards of its members.

g) Some local sections of professional societies, comprised primarily of members employed in large industries, have established "Sounding Board Groups" (including engineers in management) to improve communications between employee and employer. These have served effectively to replace nationally affiliated unions which generally are dominated by the skilled trades. The nationally affiliated unions, in struggling for job security and higher wages, too often revert to tactics such as featherbedding and monopoly of activities (e.g., only an electrician can insert an electric cord plug into an outlet) with relatively little concern for employer or the public. The engineer, as a professional employe, must not let himself stoop to such tactics, even if the employer is short-sighted in his dealings, and is seeking maximum profit with relatively little concern for employees or the public. Good management, in which the engineer (and possibly the local section of his professional society) should play an important part, acts to see that all—employee, public, and employer (who is often the public as represented by the small investor)—are treated equitably. The engineer should be the first to recognize that job security and higher earnings for employee, investor, and the public are the results of higher productivity and a spirit of cooperaation.

h) Finally, every engineer has a debt to pay for the knowledge given to him by his predecessors—to do the same for those who follow. If one cannot contribute his share to the store of knowledge, he can at least repay the debt by supporting the professional organizations which play a major part in building and preserving this heritage.

Every engineer should consider belonging to engineering societies in each of three general categories: (1) Societies such as the Founder Societies (American Society of Civil Engineers, American Institute of Mining, Metallurgical and Petroleum Engineers, American Society of Mechanical Engineers, Institute of Electrical and Electronic Engineers and the American Institute of Chemical Engineers) which function primarily in the promotion of technical knowledge in their respective broad fields of engineering; (2) Societies such as the American Concrete Institute and the American Society of Heating, Refrigerating and Air Conditioning Engineers which concern themselves primarily with their respective specialized fields of engineering (the smaller number of members in each speciality necessarily limits much local section activity to the broader fields); (3) A society such as the National Society of Professional Engineers, composed of engineers in all technical fields, with primary activities of the protection and promotion of engineering as a social and economic influence vital to the affairs of men.

A list (not all-inclusive) of National societies in engineering and related areas (including scientific and trade associations), of value in accordance with one's individual interests, is shown below. Almost all of these organizations publish journals and have annual National meetings, with a number of local sections having more frequent (generally monthly) meetings. The organizations are listed with their founding dates and an indication of their approximate total membership* where: A is a total membership greater than 40,000, B is a total membership between 20,000 and 40,000, C is a total membership between 10,000 and 20,000, D is a total membership between 5000 and 10,000, and E is a total membership less than 5000.

Acoustical Society of America 1929 (E)

American Society of Agricultural Engineers 1907 (D)

American Society of Heating, Refrigerating & Air Conditioning Engineers 1894 (B)

* From Encyclopedia of Associations, Third Edition, Detroit: Gale Research Company.

American Institute of Aeronautics and Astronautics 1930 (B)
Society of Aeronautical Weight Engineers 1939 (E)
Air Pollution Control Association 1907 (E)
Association of Asphalt Paving Technologists 1926 (E)
Audio Engineering Society 1948 (E)
American Society of Body Engineers (Automotive) 1945 (E)
Society of Automotive Engineers 1905 (B)
American Society of Bakery Engineers 1924 (E)
Society of Die Casting Engineers 1955 (E)
American Ceramic Society 1898 (D)
American Chemical Society 1876 (A)
American Institute of Chemical Engineers 1908 (C)
American Institute of Chemists 1923 (E)
American Oil Chemists Society 1909 (E)
American Society of Civil Engineers 1852 (A)
Combustion Institute 1954 (E)
Association of Computing Machinery 1947 (D)
American Concrete Institute 1905 (C)
Construction Specifications Institute 1948 (E)
American Institute of Consulting Engineers 1910 (E)
Associated General Contractors of America 1918 (D)
National Association of Corrosion Engineers 1943 (D)
American Association of Cost Engineers 1956 (E)
National Association of County Engineers 1956 (E)
Institute of Electrical & Electronic Engineers 1884 (A)
Electrochemical Society 1902 (E)
American Society for Engineering Education 1893 (D)
American Association of Engineers 1915 (D)
National Society of Professional Engineers 1934 (A)
Institute of Environmental Sciences 1957 (E)
Society of Fire Protection Engineers 1950 (E)
Institute of Food Technologists 1939 (D)
Gas Appliance Engineers Society 1955 (E)
American Geophysical Union 1919 (D)
Illuminating Engineering Society 1906 (C)
American Institute of Industrial Engineers 1948 (D)

Instrument Society of America 1939 (C)
Association of Iron and Steel Engineers 1907 (D)
American Society of Lubrication Engineers 1944 (E)
American Material Handling Society 1949 (D)
National Association of Home Builders of the United States 1942 (A)
Society for Industrial and Applied Mathematics 1952 (E)
American Society of Mechanical Engineers 1880 (A)
American Society for Metals 1913 (B)
Society of American Military Engineers 1919 (B)
American Institute of Mining, Metallurgical and Petroleum Engineers 1871 (B)
Society of Motion Picture & Television Engineers 1916 (D)
American Society of Naval Engineers 1888 (E)
Society of Naval Architects & Marine Engineers 1893 (D)
Institute of Navigation 1945 (E)
American Nuclear Society 1955 (E)
Operations Research Society 1952 (E)
Society of Packaging and Handling Engineers 1945 (E)
American Society of Photogrammetry 1934 (E)
Society of Photographic Scientists & Engineers 1947 (E)
American Physical Society 1899 (C)
American Institute of Plant Engineers 1954 (E)
Society of Plastics Engineers 1941 (D)
National Association of Power Engineers 1882 (C)
Prestressed Concrete Institute 1954 (E)
American Public Works Association 1894 (E)
American Society for Quality Control 1946 (C)
American Railway Engineering Association 1899 (E)
Society of Reproduction Engineers 1956 (E)
American Road Builder's Association 1902 (D)
American Society of Safety Engineers 1911 (D)
American Association for the Advancement of Science 1848 (A)
Federation of American Scientists 1946 (E)
Seismological Society of America 1906 (E)

Society for Social Responsibility in Science 1949 (E)
Association for Applied Solar Energy 1954 (E)
Standards Engineers Society 1947 (E)
American Statistical Association 1839 (D)
Society for Experimental Stress Analysis 1943 (E)
American Congress on Surveying and Mapping 1941 (D)
American Society for Testing Materials 1898 (C)
Society for Non-destructive Testing 1941 (E)
American Society of Tool and Manufacturing Engineers 1932 (A)
Institute of Traffic Engineers 1930 (E)
Water Pollution Control Federation 1928 (D)
American Water Works Association 1881 (C)
American Welding Society 1919 (C)
Society of Women Engineers 1949 (E)
Society of Technical Writers and Publishers 1953 (E)

4-7. CREATIVITY AND SERVICE. A professional attitude involves the primary objective of service to humanity, regardless of personal monetary compensation. This attitude does not involve merely placing the consideration of responsibility prior to the amount of monetary compensation; but also indicates an obligation to perform voluntary services for humanity without *any* monetary compensation. Voluntary service gives an unusual self-satisfaction largely because one fulfills a self-chosen purpose, instead of a purpose assigned by others. The cost of education far exceeds the tuition or fees which are charged; it is, therefore, also the duty of an educated man to repay this gift by unselfish services.

Service may be placed in the three categories of routine, ingenious, and creative. *Routine service* may be defined as a service performed in the ordinary manner that it has been performed in the past. *Ingenious service* may be defined as a service performed in a novel or unique manner. The highest form, or *creative service* is defined herewith as a service involving the self-recognition of a need for performing a good, and the fulfillment of this need. Upon the basis of the above definition, creative service is not the mere performance of a task assigned by client or employer (no matter how ingeniously it is done); nor is it the indication of how "they" could do it. Creative service involves the complete task from recognition to accomplishment, including the marshalling of whatever men, material and forces are needed for this accomplishment. Both routine and ingenious service can be either assigned or voluntary; but creative service can only be voluntary. The truly creative individual is ever alert to recognize the problems and needs of humanity. He does not wait for others to tell him what is needed, or for others to satisfy the needs; but goes forth on his own to do what needs be done. Although the greatest rewards for creative service are not monetary, the fact that creative service is always voluntary does not preclude monetary compensation; for the creative individual can in our society volunteer, with research proposals or risk capital, his new inventions or ideas for the service of humanity, which in turn may voluntarily be glad to accept and pay for these services.

The professional engineer ordinarily does not have the opportunity for the type of voluntary service that the doctor performs in treating charity patients; however, there are many opportunities for the engineer to perform voluntary services that are equally, and possibly more, important. The desire for voluntary service can and should be instilled on the college campus. It has been noted that the well-done campus voluntary service, whether performed by the honor student or the student who barely passes, generally gives the greatest of satisfactions of any college activity. Alumni coming back to the campus years later are likely to remember first and reminisce most about a voluntary service they performed as an undergraduate. Examples of voluntary services performed by engineering students at the author's campus include: setting of survey net monuments for use in future class assignments, survey and layout of track and other athletic fields, and the design and building of visual aids and laboratory equipment. An outstanding example, for which the students gave up their Christmas and between semester vacations, was the design and construction of a footbridge, across the campus lake, to connect the dormitory and classroom areas. Phases of this project included: obtaining approval from the University Administration, obtaining a permit from the City building department, testing prior to foundation design, design of the foundations and of the bridge, obtaining donations of materials and token financial support (for materials which could not be obtained by donation) from the University administration, borrowing of erection equipment, practicing for and passing County examinations for certification as welders, erection of the bridge, and arrangement and conduct of the dedication. The knowledge and experience gained and the pride of accomplishment of this type of project undoubtedly far exceeds that of efforts associated with a course for which compensation is given by means of credit and grade. Students who worked on this project, when coming back to the campus, can see a most tangible evidence of their college achievement, although it does not appear on their transcript of courses and grades nor did they inscribe their individual names on the concrete.

Voluntary service during the years of professional engineering practice (and also after retirement) can well be performed by activity in professional societies (see § 4-6) and in civic and service organizations. The professional engineer is particularly qualified, by his education and experience, to play a major role in generating and guiding activities of civic and service organizations in coping with community and national problems such as zoning, pollution, noise control, traffic, public safety, utility franchises, lighting, recreation areas and equipment, disaster relief, and conservation. The cross-membership of the individual engineer facilitates the concerted efforts of professional, civic, and service organizations in working on problems of major mutual concern.

One service organization with chapters in cities throughout the world, the Junior Chamber of Commerce (no official connection with the Chamber of Commerce), offers unique opportunities for a young man to test and develop his creative and leadership abilities. The Jaycees were founded with a constitutional prohibition against active membership after age 35; this age limit was established to help overcome what is believed to be one of the major obstacles to organizational creative endeavor. Most civic and service organizations are dominated by the respected, older leaders of a community. These older leaders have usually adjusted relatively well to whatever conditions, good or bad, exist in a community; and they tend to prefer the status quo for fear that attempting to correct one thing may possibly upset the other things which are presently quite satisfactory. When a young man proposes a significant change to an organization dominated by the elders of a community, he is typically rebuffed by such remarks as: "We can't get enough support to do it"; "Don't waste your time and ours because it's been tried many times before without success"; "It can't be done"; "Leave well enough alone." The Jaycee limitation on age gives the responsible young men of a community the opportunity, in their callow ignorance of the fact that "it can't be done" and of the magnitude of the obstacles they face, to use their sheer enthusiasm, "impractical" idealism, and "undignified" effort in city after city, year after year to do the things which "couldn't be done."

ASSIGNMENTS

4.1 Discuss the reasons for selecting your field and sub-field of engineering.

4.2 Indicate which functions of engineering particularly appeal to you, and why.

4.3 Write a short essay on what you consider to constitute success in life.

4.4 Make a list of professional, service, and civic societies which you may consider joining after graduation.

4.5 Submit a report on a voluntary service (preferably creative) project.

4.6 Prepare a topic outline to be used in preparatory study for the Engineer-in-Training examination.

BIBLIOGRAPHY

(1) Hoover, Herbert. *The Memoirs of Herbert Hoover 1874-1920*. New York: The Macmillan Company, 1951. 496 pp.

SUGGESTED ADDITIONAL READING

CONSTANCE, JOHN D. *How to Become a Professional Engineer.* New York: McGraw-Hill Book Company, Inc., 1958. 272pp.

FINCH, JAMES KIP. *Engineering and Western Civilization.* New York: McGraw-Hill Book Company, Inc., 1951. 397pp.

FINCH, JAMES KIP. *The Story of Engineering.* Garden City, New York: Doubleday & Company, Inc., 1960. 528pp.

KIRBY, RICHARD S., et al. *Engineering in History.* New York: McGraw-Hill Book Company, Inc., 1956. 530pp.

CHAPTER 5

Engineering Communications

5-1. THE OBLIGATION TO COMMUNICATE.

Unquestionably the best manner in which to repay the debt every engineer has for the knowledge given to him by his predecessors is for him to add to the body of knowledge. However, the evolving of new research, inventions, designs, or methods is incomplete unless others are made aware of the innovation. This awareness is best brought about by the presentation of technical papers at meetings of the professional societies, or publication in the professional journals.

Skill in communication, moreover, is also an everyday obligation or need. Routine correspondence, inter-office memoranda, reports, and workday conversation and discussions, all require adequate mastery for the proper fulfillment of professional duties. In a large organization information and impressions about an individual engineer obtained by upper-level administration comes essentially from written and oral reports submitted—and sometimes real ability is hidden by poor presentation of these reports.

Active participation (via communications) in civic affairs is also incumbent upon the professional engineer whose education has been directed in a manner which gives him unique abilities to recognize unwarranted conclusions, distortions of fact, and appeals to prejudice. There are too many in our society who are selling themselves or their ideas to take advantage of the ignorant, the gullible, and the public coffers; and members of the professions, particularly, must be competent and willing to speak out for the truth. The communication media for such expression includes letters to the editor, public address or debate at meetings or over radio and television, and (probably the most effective) direct communication with public officials either as an individual or as a representative of one's professional society.

The engineer in his communications generally prefers to let the facts speak for themselves, in as much as possible; but the engineer must also interpret, estimate, theorize, and predict. He must consider the possible, the probable, and the preferable to conclude and recommend what might or should be done. Most of these communications are to inform, to direct, to convince, or to persuade; but occasionally the engineer may be called upon to inspire, to entertain, or to formally accept, welcome, commemorate, or say farewell. A noteworthy derivative of the presentation of ideas to others is that it is one of the best means of both learning and clarifying one's own thoughts.

This chapter attempts to present basic principles and organization which may be applicable for the preparation and presentation of most of the above forms of communication. Particular emphasis is placed upon the technical paper and those needs of the transition from college to professional employment including the letter of application, personal resumé, and job interview. Technical papers may be prepared for student engineering publications, for presentation at student chapter meetings and contests, as well as for classroom assignments. It is hoped that every student, after having reasonable success in presenting one or more technical papers as an undergraduate, will feel confident and competent to report his future major achievements by means of professional society meetings or journals.

5-2. THE PROBLEM OF INFORMATION RE-TRIEVAL. It is estimated that the annual world-wide publications in scientific and technical fields alone include over 60,000 books, 100,000 research monographs, 55,000 professional journals containing over 1,200,000 significant articles, and over 10,000,000 reports (1:3,123). The outpouring of publications continues to rise rapidly each year. Even if one were fluent in all of the languages there would not be time, reading 24 hours a day and 365 days a year, to keep up with all the writing related to one's professional and civic interests. It has become a most difficult and frustrating problem to keep abreast of, or retrieve, even the minimum information one needs for professional and civic advancement.

The library can be as important as the laboratory in much engineering research, development and design. The rapidly expanding store of engineering information may include reports on prior work which encompasses all or most of the laboratory research or development one plans. Design and fabrication time and costs can usually be reduced by using existing standardized parts or systems. Retrieval of a single article from the library can mean a savings of days and even months of duplicating effort. Research, development, and design should start from the most advanced state of the art achieved by oneself or others. This indicates that such work should generally be preceded by a search of the literature to determine the most recent activities in the area of interest.

Much has yet to be done to aid in information retrieval, to make available the collective experience and thoughts of those who have previously worked on related problems. Advances are being made in procuring, recording, storage, and with machine processing of data. The Engineers Joint Council has taken the leadership in the compilation of an Engineering Thesaurus for maintaining control over the vocabulary of key words used in indexing, storing, and retrieving information. In addition to the Thesaurus, the Council is encouraging society publications to provide standardized abstracts and a list of key words for each article published. Increased availability and compatibility of data processing equipment, and the further development of centers specializing in each area of science and technology, should lead to greater efficiency and economy in information retrieval, dissemination, and use.

5-3. SOURCES OF ENGINEERING INFORMA-
TION. Several good guidebooks, including those by Murphey and Parke listed in Table 5-1, are available to aid in organizing

a search of the literature and in locating bibliographical material in specialized fields. A thorough search of the literature is a complex task and is generally aided by the prior preparation of a preliminary outline, which can be developed readily by obtaining a broad overview and orientation from the reading of encyclopedia or handbook articles on the subject. The preliminary outline should establish the sub-headings and tracings, or key words, needed in the search and filing of information. Notes recorded during the search are best kept on 3x5-inch or 4x6-inch cards which can be filed under the appropriate sub-heading of the preliminary outline. The individual cards should include all information needed for the bibliography and footnotes and a clear indication of which notes are direct quotations and which are paraphrased. It is most advisable also to use some form of completion symbol for each filing card, as there may be confusion between cards for sources having no appropriate items to be recorded and those uncompleted cards which include only bibliographical data of sources not available when the card was initially prepared. The following paragraphs of this section describe major general sources of engineering information, which are summarized in Table 5-1.

The starting point of a thorough library search is usually best made by a review of guides and bibliographies of bibliographies, such as those listed at the top of Table 5-1. This review should establish sources that index and abstract literature in the specialized area, as well as locate major bibliographies in the field. Indexing and abstracting services are necessarily increasing very rapidly to keep up with the expanding volume of literature, and review of these guides helps insure coverage of the major available sources in each specialized area such as *Nuclear Science Abstracts, Current Contents* (weekly guide to the Space, Electronic & Physical Sciences), *Engineer's Digest, Electrical Engineering Abstracts, Applied Mechanics Reviews, Public Health Engineering Abstracts, Technological Digests,* and many others.

The most comprehensive single source of information will usually be found in a book on the subject of interest. Books, due to the time elapsed in writing and publishing, are usually at least two to five years behind the current state of the art. The primary value of books generally is in giving a comprehensive organized summary of a large part of the major previous work in the field. A list of the books published in the English language in each subject field may be obtained from the *Cumulative Book Index.* Availability of the book from its publisher may be checked in the *Subject Guide to Books in Print.* Books not available by purchase or through loan from a local library may be borrowed by mail by members of the major professional societies from the Engineering Societies Library at the United Engineering Center in New York. Arrangements for photoprints and microfilm copy may also be made with the Library of Congress which has copies of all copyrighted U. S. books since the mid-nineteenth century. Books available in a local library are indexed by author, subject, and title in a library card catalog. An example of the author index card, which is the main entry, is shown below. Title and subject cards are identical except that either the title or subject (tracing) of the book is typed in above the author's name. Data shown on the index card are numbered and respectively described after the illustration. Search through the library stacks is facilitated by familiarity with the Dewey Decimal and Library of Congress systems of classification under either of which most U. S. libraries store and catalog their books. These classifications are listed on the following pages.

```
①        ②
  T 11      Marder, Daniel.
  .M34      ③                              ④
              The craft of technical writing.  New York, Macmillan [1960]
           ⑤
              400 p. illus.  22 cm.
           ⑥
              Includes bibliography.
           ⑦
              1. Technical writing.  2. English language-Rhetoric I. Title.
        ⑧                   ⑨              ⑩
           T 11.M34            808.066         60-5138‡
```

AUTHOR CARD

Author Card

① Call number identifying the location of storage under the system of classification.
② Author's name.
③ Title.
④ Place of publication, the publisher, and date of publication.
⑤ Number of pages, illustrations, and size of book.
⑥ Notes on the contents, bibliographies included, etc.
⑦ Tracings (additional subject entries under which this book, and related books, are listed).
⑧ Library of Congress System call number.
⑨ Dewey Decimal System call number.
⑩ Year and Library of Congress serial number.

Major classifications in the Dewey Decimal System are identified by the following numbers:

000-099 General Works (including encylopedias, periodicals)
100-199 Philosophy (including Psychology)
200-299 Religion (including Mythology)
300-399 Social Sciences
400-499 Language
500-599 Science (including Mathematics)
600-699 Useful Arts (including engineering 620-629, agriculture, aviation, etc.)
700-799 Fine Arts
800-899 Literature
910-919 Travel
920-929 Biography
900-909, 930-999 History

The major Library of Congress classifications are identified by letters of the alphabet, followed by an additional letter and/or numbers. The major classifications are:

A   General Works (including encylopedias, periodicals)
B   Philosophy & Religion
C-D   History, Auxiliary Sciences and Topography (including Biography, Numismatics, etc.)
E-F   America

G   Geography and Anthropology
H   Social Sciences (including Economics and Sociology)
J   Political Science
K   Law
L   Education
M   Music
N   Fine Arts
P   Language and Literature
Q   Science
R   Medicine
S   Agriculture and Plant and Animal Industry
T   Technology (including engineering)
U   Military Science
V   Naval Science
Z   Bibliography and Library Science

The Technology classification "T" is broken down into the following sub-classifications:

TA   Engineering (General), Civil Engineering
TC   Hydraulic Engineering
TD   Sanitary and Municipal Engineering
TE   Roads and Pavements
TF   Railroad Engineering and Operation
TG   Bridges and Roofs
TH   Building Construction
TJ   Mechanical Engineering and Machinery
TK   Electrical Engineering and Industries
TL   Motor Vehicles (including Aeronautics)
TN   Mineral Industries (including Mining and Metallurgy)
TP   Chemical Technology
TR   Photography
TS   Manufactures
TT   Trades
TX   Domestic Science

Periodicals are the major source of current information and research, and for engineering the primary indexing service is that of the *Engineering Index* which has been available since 1883.

The *Engineering Index* publishes a monthly bulletin and a yearly volume which review and abstract some 1500 periodicals, society transactions, government reports, and publications of universities, institutions and research organizations in all branches of engineering in more than 20 languages. All of the publications reviewed are available in the Engineering Societies Library. The *Applied Science and Technology Index* also issues a monthly and yearly volume which review some 200 periodicals, many of which are not included in the *Engineering Index*. *Ulrich's Periodical Directory* may list many more periodicals in each subject, and where indexed or abstracted, which are not included in either the *Engineering Index* or *Applied Science and Technology Index*. Periodical holdings of some 800 libraries are listed in *New Serials Titles*. This information is particularly valuable in order to locate holdings of lesser known periodicals such as those issued by state and municipal agencies or small local organizations. The *World List of Science Periodicals* is very comprehensive in coverage, but its use is limited by not having a subject index.

Many important engineering publications issued by government agencies are not indexed by any of the non-governmental indexing or abstracting services. Publications of the U. S. Federal government, including reports on government sponsored research, are indexed in the *Monthly Catalog of United States Government Publications* and *U. S. Government Research Reports*. Many Federal agencies also have separate indexes for their own publications. Publications of agencies of the various states, which are received by the Library of Congress, are indexed in the *Monthly Checklist of State Publications*. The United Nations and its specialized agencies publish many items of interest to engineers, mostly in the English language; these are indexed, by subject, in the *United Nations Document Index*.

Many valuable publications issued by manufacturers and other industrial organizations are not indexed by any of the previously mentioned sources. These may include company organs, catalogs giving specifications and prices of standardized products and systems, and informational and instructional pamphlets. Many local engineering libraries keep current separate files of this type of literature. The *Thomas Register of American Manufacturers* and *Kelly's Directory* for world-wide trades and manufacturers are the most comprehensive sources for determining which companies manufacture a specific product; the available literature may then be referred to in the local library, or may be obtained by correspondence with the manufacturer. Sherman's *Industrial Data Guide* is a more concise directory, similar to the *Thomas Register,* which also includes a brief bibliography related to each product. *Moody's Industrial Manual* is particularly valuable for its historical and financial data relative to each manufacturer.

Amongst the most important unpublished writings of interest to engineers are the doctoral dissertations reporting research conducted at universities. These are abstracted and indexed by subject in *Dissertation Abstracts* obtained from over 100 cooperating institutions. Microfilms may be obtained of those dissertations which are of particular interest.

Our expanding technology and problems of information retrieval seem to necessitate the increased establishment of specialized centers of research and information. Many of these organizations, with the aid of machine data processing, are in a position to be of important assistance in obtaining desired information. Directories of these organizations are listed in Table 5-1.

Table 5-1 also includes major sources of information for such other items as patents, standards and specifications, educational institutions, scholarships and awards, professional organizations, biographical data of engineers and scientists, abbreviations, signs and symbols.

5-4. DOCUMENTATION FOR ENGINEERING WRITING.

All important statements of fact which are not generally accepted as true or common knowledge should be supported by evidence for their validity. If the writer is not presenting verifiable evidence from his own work or experimentation, then his indebtedness for such evidence taken from the works of others should be acknowledged. Additional sources of information,

Table 5-1

MAJOR SOURCES OF ENGINEERING INFORMATION

Item	Major Sources
Guides & Bibliographies of Bibliographies	1. Dalton, Blanche H. *Sources of Engineering Information.* Berkeley: University of California Press, 1948. 109 pp.—A compilation of worldwide sources, by field, including bibliographies, reference books, indexes, abstracts, standards and specifications. 2. *Guide to Reference Books.* Chicago: American Library Association.—Indexes, by subject, worldwide reference works including bibliographies, handbooks, abstracts, guides, yearbooks, atlases, dictionaries, catalogs, indexes, encyclopedias, etc. 3. Murphey, Robert W. *How and Where to Look it Up.* New York: McGraw-Hill Book Company, Inc., 1958. 721 pp.—Includes lists of reference books, bibliographies of bibliographies, indexes, etc. in specialized fields, and also notes on use of library and preparation of research papers. 4. Parke, Nathan Grier, III. *Guide to the Literature of Mathematics and Physics Including Related Works in Engineering Science,* 2nd Rev. Ed. New York: Dover Publications, Inc., 1958. 436 pp.—Includes comprehensive discussion of literature searching and list, by subject, of texts, reference works, bibliographies, indexes, and abstracts. 5. Besterman, Theodore. *A World Bibliography of Bibliographies.* New York: The Scarecrow Press, Inc., 1959.—Includes lists, by subjects, of separately published bibliographies, with annotation in the language of publication. 6. *Bibliographic Index.* New York: The H. M. Wilson Company—Cumulatively indexes, by subject, bibliographies ranging from comprehensive separately published books to a current periodical article which includes a list of a dozen or so references. 7. *Index Bibliographicus Vol. I Science and Technology.* Paris: United Nations Educational, Scientific and Cultural Organization, 1952.—A world-wide directory listing, by subject, bibliographical and abstracting periodicals.
Books	1. *Library Card Catalog*—Index by author, title, and subject of books available in local library.

Table 5-1 (Continued)

Item	Major Sources
	2. *Cumulative Book Index.* New York: The H. M. Wilson Company—Indexes books in English language (worldwide) by subject, author and title. 3. *Subject Guide to Books in Print.* New York: R. R. Bowker Company—Indexes annually books from some 1300 publishers, by subject. 4. *Scientific, Medical and Technical Books Published in the United States of America.* Washington: National Academy of Sciences—National Research Council, 1958. —Includes annotated list of major U. S. books in engineering, science, medicine, agriculture, forestry, etc.
Periodicals	1. *Engineering Index.* New York: Engineering Index, Inc. —Indexes, by subject, articles in some 1500 current engineering, scientific, and industrial publications thruout the world. 2. *Applied Technology Index* (formerly Industrial Arts Index). New York: The H. W. Wilson Company.— Indexes articles, by subject, in some 200 engineering and trade periodicals. 3. *Ulrich's Periodical Directory.* New York: R. R. Bowker Company, 1963.—Lists, by subject, some 16,000 worldwide periodicals including where indexed or abstracted. 4. *New Serial Titles.* Washington, D. C.: Library of Congress. Supplementing: *Union List of Serials.* New York: The H. M. Wilson Company.—Lists holdings of some 800 libraries of over 150,000 titles. Contact may be made with the indicated library if a desired periodical is not available in one's local library. 5. *World List of Science Periodicals Published in the Years 1900-1950.* 3rd Edition. New York: Academic Press Inc., 1952.—Bibliography of some 50,000 periodicals, and holdings in some 250 libraries.
Government Publications	1. *Monthly Catalog of United States Government Publications.* Washington, D. C.: U. S. Government Printing Office.—Indexes monthly by agencies and annually by subject publications of the Federal government. 2. *U. S. Government Research Reports* (U. S. Department of Commerce Office of Technical Services). Washington, D. C.: U. S. Government Printing Office.—Issued twice

Table 5-1 (Continued)

Item	Major Sources
	a month to announce reports on research and development released by the Army, Navy, Atomic Energy Commission and other Government agencies.
	3. *Monthly Checklist of State Publications.* Washington, D. C.: U. S. Government Printing Office.—Indexes, by subject, publications of individual state agencies, which are received by the Library of Congress. Includes publications of Engineering Experiment Stations of Universities.
	4. *United Nations Documents Index.* New York: United Nations.—Indexes, by subject, publications of the United Nations and Specialized Agencies.
Products and Industrial Organizations	1. *Thomas Register of American Manufacturers.* New York: Thomas Publishing Co.—Comprehensive list of manufacturers classified by products, including trade names.
	2. *Moody's Industrial Manual.* New York: Moody's Investor Service, Inc.—Comprehensive data on major industrial enterprises including history, finances, products, and principal plants.
	3. *Kelly's Directory of Merchants, Manufacturers and Shippers.* London: Kelly's Directories Ltd.—Directory covering over 125 countries, listing by trades and products.
	4. Sherman, M. *Industrial Data Guide.* New York: The Scarecrow Press, 1962.—Lists manufacturers and related books and periodical articles for each product.
Doctoral Dissertations	1. *Dissertation Abstracts.* Ann Arbor, Michigan: University Microfilms, Inc.—A subject compilation of abstracts of doctoral dissertations from over 100 cooperating institutions, which are available on microfilm.
Information Centers and Research Organizations	1. *Directory of University Research Bureaus and Institutes.* Detroit: Gale Research Company—Guide listing some 1200 organizations in U. S. and Canadian Universities, performing research in engineering, science, and other fields.
	2. *Specialized Science Information Services in the United States.* Washington, D. C.: National Science Foundation (NSF 61-68, November, 1961)—Includes data on some 400 organizations or projects providing information service beyond periodic publications.

Table 5-1 (Continued)

Item	Major Sources
	3. *Industrial Research Laboratories of the United States.* Washington, D. C.: National Academy of Sciences— National Research Council.—Indexes, by subject, and describes some 5000 non-governmental laboratories devoted to research, including development of products and processes.
Patents	1. *U. S. Department of Commerce Patent Office Manual of Classifications.* Washington, D. C.: U. S. Government Printing Office.—Lists numbers and descriptive titles of some 300 classes and 57,000 subclasses.
	2. *Index of Patents Issued from the United States Patent Office.* Washington, D. C.: U. S. Government Printing Office.—Annual index by patentees and classifications.
	3. *Official Gazette of the United States Patent Office.*— Weekly review of patents granted, notices, decisions, etc.
Standards and Specifications	1. *Index of Federal Specifications, Standards and Handbooks.* Washington, D. C.: U. S. Government Printing Office.—Indexes the available Federal Military and General Services Administration specifications, standards, and handbooks.
	2. *Index to ASTM Standards.* Philadelphia: American Society for Testing Materials.—Indexes, by subject, the ASTM specifications and test methods.
	3. *National Directory of Commodity Specifications* (National Bureau of Standards). Washington, D. C.: U. S. Government Printing Office.—Indexes, by subject, and describes the standards and specifications of trade associations, technical societies, government agencies, and industrial organizations.
	4. *Catalog of American Standards.* New York: American Standards Association.—Annual issue of the *Magazine of Standards* indexing some 2000 American Standards and some 300 International Recommendations.
Educational Institutions	1. *American Universities and Colleges.* Washington, D. C.: American Council on Education.—Includes general report on higher education and data on some 1000 U. S. Institutions.
	2. *Universities of the World Outside U.S.A.* Washington, D. C.: American Council on Education.—Includes gen-

Table 5-1 (Continued)

Item	Major Sources
	eral discussion and data on institutions in some 70 countries. 3. *Commonwealth Universities Yearbook.* London: The Association of Universities of the British Commonwealth. —Includes data on some 200 institutions which are or were in the British Commonwealth. 4. *International Handbook of Universities.* Paris: The International Association of Universities.—Includes data on institutions in some 70 countries outside of the U.S.A. and British Commonwealth.
Scholarships and Awards	1. *Handbook of Scientific and Technical Awards in the United States and Canada 1900-1952.* New York: Special Libraries Association.—A compilation of the most important awards presented by scientific and technical societies, listed by societies. 2. "A Compilation of Financial Aid for Graduate Study in Engineering" *The Council Bulletin of the Tau Beta Pi Association* (R. H. Nagel, Editor, University of Tennessee).—Annual Index summary of financial aid available for engineering graduate studies. 3. *A Guide to Graduate Study.* Washington, D. C.: American Council on Education.—Includes general discussion of graduate study and data, listed by institutions, on graduate programs and financial aid. 4. *Fellowships in the Arts and Sciences.* Washington, D. C.: American Council on Education.—Current catalog of financial aid for graduate students, from sources other than educational institutions. 5. *Handbook on International Study.* New York: Institute of International Education.—Includes information on financial aid, regulations, services, and educational institutions thruout the world. 6. Burckell, C. E. *The College Blue Book—Book Four.* Yonkers, N. Y.: The College Blue Book, 1962.—Lists Scholarships, Fellowships, Grants, Stipends, Prizes, Assistance, Aids, Awards, Loans, Etc. available to American students and scholars. 7. Feingold, S. N. *Scholarships, Fellowships, and Loans.* Cambridge, Mass.: Bellman Publishing Co.—Lists alphabetically by administering agency, including index by field.

Table 5-1 (Continued)

Item	Major Sources
Professional Organizations	1. *Encyclopedia of Associations.* Detroit: Gale Research Company.—Guide to some 6000 engineering, scientific, business, professional, labor, trade, educational, fraternal and social organizations in the U. S. 2. *Scientific and Technical Societies of the United States and Canada.* Washington, D. C.: National Academy of Sciences.—National Research Council.—Presents detailed information on some 1800 organizations. 3. Bates, R. S. *Scientific Societies in the United States.* New York: Columbia University Press, 1958. 297 pp.—Traces historical development from 18th century; includes bibliography on history of each organization (includes many local engineering societies). 4. *Directory of International Scientific Organizations.* Paris: United Nations Educational, Scientific and Cultural Organization, 1953. 312 pp.—Describes some 260 organizations having primary international scope. Note: See also "Abbreviations of. . . . ." at end of table.
Biographical Data	1. *Who's Who in Engineering.* New York: Lewis Historical Publishing Company.—A biographical dictionary of the engineering profession. 2. *Who Knows—and What.* Chicago: A. N. Marquis Company.—Includes biographical sketches of experts and specialists in various specialized fields of knowledge. 3. *American Men of Science.* Tempe, Arizona: The Jacques Cattel Press.—A biographical directory of scientists and engineers. 4. *Biography Index.* New York: The H. W. Wilson Company.—A cumulative index to biographical material in books and magazines. Note: See also membership directories of the various professional societies.
Abbreviations, Signs and Symbols	1. Zimmerman, O. T., and Lavine, I. *Scientific and Technical Abbreviations, Signs, and Symbols.* Dover, New Hampshire: Industrial Research Service, 1949. 541 pp.—Includes general list and also those of American Standards Association and other organizations. 2. *World List of Abbreviations of Scientific, Technological and Commercial Organizations.* New York: Hafner Publishing Co., 1960. 300 pp.—Includes abbreviations for some 2500 organizations thruout the world.

cross-references, and aside amplifying discussion (which may otherwise complicate or interrupt) are also helpful supplements to engineering writing. The above documentation of engineering literature is accomplished by means of reference indexes, footnotes, and a bibliography.

Unless the contrary is clearly expressed, the quotation of another's conclusions or opinions usually indicates agreement or acceptance. If this quoted material includes obsolete concepts, fallacies or prejudice, one's own writing becomes suspect of the same. Care must therefore be used in selecting material, even from the writings of those considered expert in the field, particularly where there may be obsolescence.

Direct quotations should be enclosed in double quotation marks (" "); however, some writers use only indentation and single spacing for quoted passages having a length exceeding three lines. Where double quotation marks are used, a quotation within the quotation should be enclosed by single quotation marks (' '). Omissions, which do not alter the original meaning of a lengthy quotation, may be indicated by ellipses, or periods alternating with spaces (. . .). If the omitted material follows the end of a sentence, three dots ordinarily are used in addition to the period that ends the sentence. Where the omission is a full paragraph or more, alternating periods and spaces are extended across the page. If the writer wishes to insert comments or corrections in the body of a quotation, such interpolation may be done by inserting in square brackets [ ] at the proper point. Statements to be quoted which are received orally should be submitted for approval of the person being quoted, prior to inclusion. If it is not practical to consult the original source first hand and a quotation or data is taken from another writer who is quoting from the original, it is a good precaution against risking or compounding mistakes to indicate that the quotation or data is cited by another and is therefore from a secondary source. Quotation marks are also used for slang or ironical words, unusual technical words, a word to which one wants to direct attention, a word accompanied by its definition, and titles of papers or chapters of books.

The forms in which reference sources are listed in a bibliography will be found to differ slightly amongst various writers. The essentials of a bibliography are to include in a consistent manner information such as the author's name, title of book or periodical article, place and name of publisher or name of periodical, date of publication, and total number of pages in the book or volume number and pages of the periodical article. A bibliographical listing of a patent should include the name of the patentee, title, country, number, date of issue, and name of the assignee, if any. The bibliographical listings should be in alphabetical order and placed at the end of the article, thesis, chapter, or in an appendix. Annotations are sometimes added, as in Table 5-1, to indicate the value and relation of each bibliographical entry to the subject of the study. Sample suggested forms for typical bibliographical listings are shown below in alphabetical order:*

BIBLIOGRAPHY

(1) DALTON, BLANCHE H. *Sources of Engineering Information.* Berkeley: University of California Press, 1948. 109 pp.
[Book by a single author]

(2) DESCARTES, RENÉ. *Rules for the Direction of the Mind.* Translated by E. S. Haldane and G. R. T. Ross (*Great Books of the Western World,* 31:1-40) Chicago: Encyclopaedia Britannica, Inc., 1952.
[Translated work, part of a series]

(3) FAIRES, VIRGIL M. and WINGREN, ROY M. *Problems on the Design of Machine Elements.* 3rd ed.; New York: The Macmillan Company, 1955. 148 pp.
[Book by two authors]

(4) GILMAN, W. E., et al. *The Fundamentals of Speaking.* New York: The Macmillan Company, 1951. 608 pp.
[Book by 3 or more authors]

(5) *Light Gage Cold-Formed Steel Design Manual.* New York:

---

* For typewritten manuscripts, italicized sections should be designated by *underlining;* italics are used for titles of books, periodicals, newspapers, published documents, and also for emphasis of first occurrence of terms with special meanings.

American Iron and Steel Institute, 1962. 127 pp.

[Book where authorship not specified]

(6) NEWMARK, N. W. "Influence Charts for Computation of Stresses in Elastic Foundations," *University of Illinois Engineering Experiment Station Bulletin 338,* 1942. cited in Urquhart, Leonard C. (ed.), *Civil Engineering Handbook.* 3rd ed.; New York: McGraw-Hill Book Company, 1950. 1002 pp.

[Edited work as secondary source]

(7) "Pliers," *Federal Specification GGG-P-471c,* January 8, 1960.

[Specification]

(8) SEGRÉ, E. "Transuranic Elements," *The Encylopedia Americana,* 1958 Edition, XXVII, 12e-13.

[Signed article in encyclopedia]

(9) SPEAKMAN, EUGENE R. "Sealed Hinge." United States Patent Office #3,075,234, January 29, 1963 (assigned to Douglas Aircraft Company, Inc.)

[Patent]

(10) TAYLOR, JAMES I. "Effective Teaching of Professionalism," *Civil Engineering,* **32**:40-41, October, 1962.

[Periodical article]

(11) U. S. Bureau of the Census. *U. S. Census of Population: 1960. Number of Inhabitants, United States Summary.* Final Report PC(1)—1A. Washington, D. C.: U. S. Government Printing Office, 1961.

[Document]

(12) Washington Wire in *The Wall Street Journal,* September 7, 1964.

[Newspaper Article]

(13) WISEMAN, H. A. B. "Behavior of Aluminum Alloys Subjected to Combined Stresses." Unpublished Ph.D. dissertation, The Pennsylvania State University, 1954. 203 pp.

[Unpublished Material]

Reference indexes should be placed after the punctuation mark (comma or period) ending the material, or immediately after the statement or data to be verified. Footnote reference figures or symbols usually are superscript numerals placed one-half space above the line; these may either be numbered consecutively for the entire manuscript or chapter, or each page having footnotes may start anew with the number 1. Numbering consecutively throughout the entire manuscript may necessitate considerable renumbering, if later additions are made to the sequence of footnotes. To avoid confusion in the instance of tabular, algebraic, or numerical data it is preferable to use symbols such as the asterik (*), dagger (†), double dagger (‡), section mark (§), or number sign (#); if more symbols are needed, each of these may be doubled, e.g., **, ††.

The typical form for footnote entries differs from bibliographical form primarily in the designation of the exact page of the referenced statement or fact, instead of the total number of pages in the reference source. Some writers prefer a form for footnotes that lists the author's given name or initials first, instead of the surname. In the more formal type of writing both footnotes and bibliography are used, with the footnotes being placed at the bottom of the page where the referenced item appears. Sometimes, where space and printing costs are at a premium, footnotes only are used.

When references to the same source follow closely and uninterruptedly, *ibid,* (for *ibidem,* "in the same place") may be used for that part of the information which is identical to that which precedes. If a reference is exactly identical (including page number) to one which immediately precedes, *loc. cit.* (for *loco citato,* "in the place cited") may be used; if the identical reference is followed closely but is not immediately preceding, both the author's surname and *loc. cit.* are used. When reference is to be made to a different page of a source previously cited but not immediately preceding, *op. cit.* (for *opere citato,* "in the work cited") with the new page number and author's surname may be used. It is most annoying if one has to search many prior pages to find a previous citation, so that these abbreviations should be used judiciously and sparingly. A sequence of footnotes which illustrates the use of these abbreviations is shown.

[1] Sherman, M. *Industrial Data Guide*. New York: The Scarecrow Press, 1963, p. 127

[2] *Ibid.,* p. 26.

[3] Dalton, Blanche H. *Sources of Engineering Information.* Berkeley: University of California Press, 1948, p. 3

[4] Sherman, *loc. cit.*

[5] Sherman, *op. cit.,* p. 83

Other abbreviations commonly used for reference purposes include the following:

circa (about)

cf. (for *confer,* "compare")

cf. ante (for *confer ante,* "compare above")

cf. post (for *confer post,* "compare after")

ed. (edited, editor, edition)

e.g. (for *exempli gratia,* "for example")

et al (for *et alii,* "and others")

f., ff. (and the following page or pages)

i.e. (for *id est,* "that is")

infra (below)

n.d. (no date given)

n.n. (no name given)

n.p. (no place or publisher given)

n.s. (new series)

p., pp. (page, pages)

passim (in various passages)

q.v. (for *quod vide,* "which see")

sc. (for *scilicet,* "namely" or "to wit")

sic. (thus—used within brackets to indicate that a quotation is given literally, though containing an irregularity or misstatement)

supra (above)

s.v. (for *sub verbo* or *voce,* "under a word or heading")

tr. (translated, translator)

vide (see)

viz. (for videlicet, "namely" or "to wit")

vol., vols. (volume, volumes)

A concise reference index system, which eliminates footnotes and requires only bibliographical entries, is also used frequently in engineering and scientific writing. In this method a reference index such as (3:67-68) is placed directly after the statement or passage being quoted, and at the same level as the type. The numeral "3" in the reference index refers to the third reference listed in the bibliography (bibliographical entries are all numbered when this system is used); the numbers "67-68" refer to the specific page numbers from which the statement is quoted. For short periodical articles, newspaper articles, patents, etc., the reference index may be shown as a single number such as (5), referring to the fifth entry in the bibliography. This latter reference index system is used throughout this text.

5-5. PRINCIPLES OF ENGINEERING COMMU-NICATION.   The general area of engineering communication includes the use of written prose, mathematics, drawings, graphs, and oral presentations. It is assumed that the reader is already familiar [or can readily refer to sources, e.g., (2), (3), for details] with elements of these such as the rules of grammer, the preparation of outlines, etc.; and this section primarily reviews and extends those principles which may be of particular assistance in the applications presented herewith.

The author firmly believes, after working with some 1000 engineering students over a period of 15 years, that almost every engineer can write and speak reasonably well on a subject about which he is knowledgable and enthusiastic, provided he is willing to follow a few principles and apply the necessary effort to organize his work. Although many will argue that good writing and speaking are rare, it should and can be within the abilities of almost every professional engineer to be able to write and speak in an acceptable manner.

There are many different styles of writing and speaking used and accepted in engineering communication. However, the various styles usually follow a common set of principles similar to those listed below, in order to meet the general requirements for **pre-**sentation at a professional society meeting and subsequent publication:

1. Be precise and coherent. This is the most difficult principle to apply in that it requires considerable judgment and experience to confine the scope of a topic to that which best fits the allotted time, space, and audience. The inexperienced writer or speaker often tends to choose too broad a scope for his topic and then has great difficulty maintaining coherence or pertinence. Thus if one were asked to give a half-hour talk on a recent occupational assignment, obviously it could not be done effectively if the topic to be presented was "Engineering." Even if successively narrowed down to "Civil Engineering," then "Structures," then "Concrete Structures," then "Prestressed Concrete Structures"—the latter still is broad enough to need several books to cover the topic adequately. Still further successive narrowing of scope could be "Post-tensioned Prestressed Concrete Structures," then "Anchorage Devices in Post-tensioned Prestressed Concrete Structures," and finally one that might be covered in a half hour: "Shrink Fitted Anchorage Devices in Post-tensioned Prestressed Concrete Structures."

2. Be Clear. The amount of background material given and the vocabulary chosen should be adapted to the audience, which may vary from experts in the field, to engineers having experience only in distantly related fields, to laymen. Regardless of the audience one should choose words that are simple and direct; prefer the familiar to the far-fetched, the concrete expression to the abstract, and the short word to the long. Most words can be interpreted in a number of ways; possible misunderstanding by the audience should be anticipated and definitions given, at least for key words. As many engineering communications become permanent reference material, it is important to use specific dates instead of relative time elements such as "this month," "recently," or "in the near future," which become meaningless with the passage of time. Modern trends in grammatical construction emphasize the prime need for clarity of expression, instead of rules;

however, it is usually necessary to follow most of the rules in order to obtain the desired clarity of expression. The insertion of headings and subheadings helps to separate into more digestible smaller parts.

3. Be Concise. In the light of the vast amount of literature pouring forth today, a style of writing which facilitates rapid reading and economy of time and space is particularly dictated. Wordy phrases or statements are not always objectionable as there may be justifiable reasons of gaining additional emphasis or clarity. However, there are patterns of wordy phrases which tend frequently (and usually unnecessarily) to creep into engineering communications. Examples of a number of these, and concise substitutes for each, are given below:

Wordy	*Concise*
a small percentage of	few
an insufficient number of	too few
all of the	all
as a whole	entire
at that particular time	then
at the present time	now
by means of	by, with
due to the fact that	because, since
for the purpose of	to
has resulted in a reduction of	has reduced
in order to	to
in the course of	while
in the event of	if
in the majority of instances	usually
is considerable doubt concerning	is uncertain
is provided with	has
it is clear that	clearly
it is obvious that	obviously
it should be understood that	understand that
it very frequently happens that	often
make the adjustment	adjust
most of the time	usually

4. Be Objective. Engineering communications should, in so far as possible, let the facts and evidence speak for themselves dispassionately, without exaggeration or excess enthusiasm. Either laudatory or derogatory references to personalities should be avoided. Emphasis should be placed upon the subject matter, not the author, by using the third person;* that is, avoiding the personal pronouns "I," "me," "we," "us," and "my." In those rare instances where it is difficult to avoid the injection of personality, it is possible to circumvent the use of the first person: "In my opinion . . ." or "I believe . . ." can be restated, "In the writer's opinion . . ." or "The author believes . . ."

5. Qualify Statements. It is rare, if not impossible, to know something to be a certainty—what is usually known are varying degrees of probability. That is, the evidence does not "prove" but "indicates," to some degree of probability. The engineer should recognize both in communication and daily work that uncertainty and exception abound, and that most quantities are measured only by their relative values. Statements in the absolute sense including words such as "never," "always," or "will" (referring to an indefinite and uncertain future) should be avoided. The engineer can no more assume that there is nothing between black and white, between hero and villian, or between his way and their way than he can assume that there is nothing between zero and infinity. Developing the habit of qualifying one's statements brings about a greater awareness of relative values, exceptions, and uncertainties thereby reducing the probability of failures due to oversight in professional work. Examples of some absolute statements, and qualified alternatives, are shown below:

Absolute	Qualified
It never happens	It has not been known to happen
It will undoubtedly perform well	Investigation indicates it should perform well
It was found to be ideal	It appeared satisfactory in all important aspects
It will arrive next month	It is expected to arrive next month

6. Prefer the Positive. Beginning with a negative argument tends to provoke opposition, emotions and face saving in others,

---

* Some engineers contend that writing in the *first person* is acceptable and preferable because it is more concise and less stilted.

which even the best logic probably will not overcome. It is preferable to start on a common ground of positive agreement, pose the problem, and go through a step-by-step solution together with the audience. Statements made in a positive sense also generally lead both to conciseness and definiteness. Examples of some wordy negative phrases, and alternatives stated in the positive, are shown below:

Wordy Negative	*Concise Positive*
It is not very often on time	It is usually late
did not have much confidence in	distrusted
did not pay any attention to	ignored

7. Use Standard Notation and Consistent Form. It is an imposition on the reader if an already established notation or language is changed. The use of symbols and abbreviations such as those recommended by the American Standards Association, and a consistent form as recommended in manuals of style facilitate the use and understanding of communications. Some general recommendations for the use of numbers in written communications are given below:

- *a*) Spell out if at the start of a sentence or if one of two successive numbers (e.g., there are twenty 2″ long pieces)
- *b*) Spell out fractions if indefinite or approximate (e.g., one-half of the amount; the item is ½″ long)
- *c*) Use comma for numbers only above four digits (e.g., 2329; 23,290)

8. Watch for Misspelling and Explicit Repetition. A dictionary and thesaurus are necessary tools for establishing the correct spelling and meaning of words and avoiding excessive repetition of the same words or their derivatives (e.g., It is proposed, shortly, to make the assembly line shorter). Incorrect spelling gives an impression of carelessness or ignorance that may cause the reader to question the correctness of the results and conclusions being presented. Final responsibility for the correctness of a report rests with the writer; this responsibility includes that of final proofreading to correct the mistakes in spelling or meaning which may be contributed by the typist.

5-6. ORGANIZATION OF ENGINEERING WRITING. The most important part of engineering writing usually does not get printed—that is, the outline. It establishes the orderly plan, the dominant element, in the various recommended stages of the writing process. These stages include:

(1) Recognition of the problem and preparation of a preliminary outline. The preliminary outline should be a function of the length and type of writing (e.g., report, book) and the audience to which it is pointed.

(2) Search of the literature and gathering of data, which may include experimentation. During this stage it is most helpful to keep an "idea page" to jot down useful information or ideas, immediately upon conception, for later incorporation in the first draft.

(3) Classification and evaluation of acquired data under a revised more comprehensive outline.

(4) Rapid writing stage (first draft). During this stage it is usually best not to worry about sentence structure, spelling, punctuation and the like; these can cause undue distraction from the main task, which, in the first stage of production, is to get thoughts on paper in any language at any time.

(5) Review and rewrite. The review and rewrite is best preceded by laying the work aside for at least a day; during this period one might seek reading and criticism by others, particularly to check ambiguity and basic concepts.

(6) Check final typing and assembly.

There are a number of elemental questions that a report or article should usually be organized to answer: what? who? when? where? why? how? cost? safe? The general approaches under which these elemental questions may be answered and the writing organized are (separate sections of a lengthy work may each use different approaches):

Deductive—starting with statements and illustrating these statements by examples.

Inductive—starting with observations and facts, which lead to a conclusion. This approach is best for convincing or persuasion, when the audience may be prejudiced against the conclusion, as it leads up to the conclusion gradually.

Chronological—approaching in the sequence of time in which events occurred or are planned.

Psychological—stating the familiar before the unfamiliar, the pleasant before the unpleasant (e.g., delaying indication of the need for more money or manpower).

Reports or articles may be organized to consist of the following parts:

1. A title or title page which may include:
   a) Title of the report or article, with any necessary subheads;
   b) Name of the organization or individual which authorized or published the work;
   c) Name of the writer or writers and their positions, titles, memberships, and degrees;
   d) Date of submission or publication, and in the instance of a report an assigned number.
2. A foreword (or preface) or letter of transmittal which may act as a concise introduction to the report or article. It may contain a statement of purpose, instructions for use, notification of status, authorizations, limiting factors of the investigation, recommendations and references for, and acknowledgments to those who were of assistance. If effectively written, it can motivate to read further and can point out sections of particular import.

3.   A table of contents (not usually needed for short articles or reports) indicating the major sections or subheadings, and the pages where they may be found. The table of contents at the beginning of this text may be referred to as an example.

4.   An abstract of the report or article giving the major points in a minimum of words (normally not to exceed 5 per cent of the original). The abstract ordinarily should serve as a brief and complete summary, not merely a preview or table of contents, with emphasis on meaningful explanations of results and conclusions. The abstract may serve as a guide for information retrevial, reviews by newspapers and periodicals, and a means for the busy executive to keep up with the work being done. Abstracts serving such a wide audience should be written so that comprehension of the major concepts and conclusions may be possible without further reading and expressed in a manner so that even those not too familiar with the subject can understand. Information retrieval personnel appear to prefer abstracts prepared primarily for retrieval purposes to be only a preview, to encourage reading of the original source material.

5.   The body of the article or report which may include:

     a) A statement of the problem and scope of the investigation or study;

     b) A resumé of previous work in the field;

     c) Definitions of key terms;

     d) Theories and principles involved in the problem under discussion;

     e) Details of analysis, description of equipment used, and essential steps in the procedure or method of investigation;

     f) Results, including computations or tabulated data, with clear indications of the accuracy involved;

     g) Conclusions, interpretation, evaluation, and recommendations including that of future studies or work needed.

6.   A bibliography of original source material used in writing the report or article.

7.   An appendix including supplementary materials that are of aid in clarifying the data, but not considered essential for understanding. These may consist of additional charts, maps, otherwise inaccessible documents, lengthy quotations, detailed derivations, original data, etc., each forming a separate appendix heading.

Most people today have far more literature crossing their desks than there is time available for thorough reading, or even perusal. Quick decisions are made, as a piece of literature is encountered, to read it, route it, or reject it. Good writing should facilitate this type of decision; and when prepared for a varied audience should point specific parts of the report or article for particular categories of audience. These categories of audience might be (a) coworkers and other specialists in the field, (b) engineers and scientists working in other related fields, (c) upper-level management (non-engineering) and the lay public.

Upper-level management and the public would tend to be primarily interested in reading the type of material that would be in the abstract (part 4, above). Engineers and scientists in related fields would tend to be primarily interested in the conclusions, broad general approach, and bases for decisions; this type of information might be obtained by reading only the abstract, foreword (introduction), and possibly the detailed conclusions and recommendations included in the body of the report (part 5g). Coworkers and specialists in the field would normally be interested in reading the entire report or article, with the possible exception of the appendices. The above relations of the parts of an article or report to a potential audience are summarized in Fig. 5-1 where circumscribing boxes confine the parts of probable major concern to each category of audience.

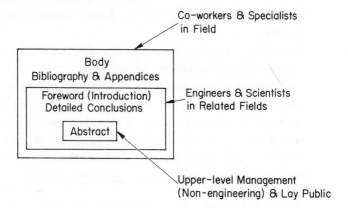

Fig. 5-1 Report or Article Parts of Major Concern to
Each Category of Audience

5-7. ENGINEERING SPEAKING. Speeches may generally be classified into four types:

(1) Verbatim—A speech which is previously written out in its entirety and read, word for word, to the audience. It is a rare individual who can do this type of speech well; the usual result is a dull, sleep-inducing monotone. Unfortunately, this type of speech is still encountered quite frequently at engineering professional meetings. Many people find this type of speech particularly irritating when the entire speech is also made available in printed form for the audience. As one can read much faster than words can be spoken, most of the audience have finished reading the speech (if handed out prior for convenience or for reference to figures) long before the speaker is finished. If the speaker contributes nothing beyond what is printed, many people feel that their time has been imposed upon, as they could read the paper at their own leisure in considerably less time. The primary justification for a verbatim speech may be when very delicate matters are being discussed and only well-thought-out, carefully, and precisely worded statements will suffice for

the entire speech. If only part of a speech requires precise wording, it would be preferable to limit the verbatim reading to that part.

(2) Memorized—A speech which is previously written out in its entirety and presented, word for word, from memory. This type of speech also rarely can be done well, particularly if it involves a considerable length of time. It is a relatively great burden upon the speaker to prepare for this type of speech, and the usually stilted results are not at all commensurate with the effort involved.

(3) Impromptu—A speech given without any prior preparation. This type of speech would generally be limited to unexpected occasions for which there is no time to prepare.

(4) Extemporaneous—A speech in which most of the exact language is fashioned as one goes, with the aid of prepared notes or a memorized outline. This is generally the most effective type of speech and the type that most engineers should attempt to concentrate their efforts upon. The important techniques involved in speaking well extemporaneously to a group are essentially the same as those involved in making good individual conversation, for the group is composed of individuals. The basic extemporaneous speech may include segments which are memorized, impromptu, or read verbatim.

Preparation for a speech might very well be similar to the preparation involved in a written article or report on the same subject. Usually the verbatim or memorized speech is written out in full in a form which would be acceptable for publication. However, some adjustments may be necessary for the details of heavy mathematics, massive statistics, etc., which can be understood by a reading audience but which would be difficult to assimiliate in the rapid sequence of a verbal presentation. If time allows, it is also well to write out in full a speech to be presented extemporaneously, as concepts and vocabulary choice can thereby be reinforced. Courtesy dictates that the speech be timed beforehand, under simulated speaking conditions, to hold it within the allotted portion of the program. Prior arrangements should also be made with the program chairman if a podium, projector, blackboard, etc., are needed.

The introduction, by others, of a speaker may range from a bare or simple announcement to an excess of laudatory adjectives; or the speaker may be used as the butt of an anecdote which may range from complimentary to raw, insulting humor. It is well to be prepared (if necessary, by memorizing) to respond at least to the extremes of the types of introduction.

Improved effectiveness in public speaking comes about primarily from practice, pointing up the importance of obtaining experience by the presentation of papers before student organizations. The first time that one speaks before a large audience will almost always be an occasion of high nervous tension. Succeeding appearances are much easier, but most speakers continue to feel those twinges of nervousness prior to appearing before each new audience. Usually, the speaker who knows and is enthusiastic about his subject is relatively at ease after getting past the initial remarks; these initial remarks may be memorized or read verbatim as an aid to overcoming the higher opening tensions.

If the speaker does not show enthusiasm about his subject, it is unlikely that the audience will be enthusiastic, or even interested. The deadpan approach can be broken, as the minimum facial animation, with an occasional smile; the smile, as a symbol of friendliness, is also closely associated with interest and enthusiasm. Most people feel that a sincere individual will look them in the eye, not continually at notes, floor or walls. Talking to the audience also is important to note the reactions of individuals and thereby determine the probable need for repetition, clarification, or emphasis.

Visual aids, such as blackboard, slides, movies, maps, charts, distributed data, and demonstration equipment (the demonstration equipment should be checked out beforehand to determine if it functions), are valuable aids for both holding audience atten-

tion and supplementing the spoken word. Whereas certain man-
nerisms and motions of the speaker should be watched for and
eliminated, the natural use of appropriate standard internationally
recognized gestures can be a very effective aid. Well-known standard gestures include the following:

a) Pointing with the forefinger—for visual emphasis;
b) Open hand, palm up—for offering and accepting;
c) Open hand, palm vertical—for limitation or demarcation;
d) Open hand, palm moving down or away—to reject, or
   minimize;
e) Clenched fist—for strong emphasis, defiance.

Most professional-society meeting papers are presented by the
speaker without audience interruption, and at the conclusion of
the paper a short period is allowed for discussion or defense of
the paper. If the speaker himself is to request questions from the
audience, adequate time should be allowed (before assuming no
questions are forthcoming) as the first question is often slow to
come. Repetition of the question gives one time to think, and, in
a large auditorium where the speaker has the only microphone,
repetition is appropriate for those who may not have heard the
question. It may also be desirable to reformulate the question for
clarity and ease in answering. Questions should be answered without belligerency, in the spirit of scientific inquiry; and as even the
wisest man is ignorant of many things, one should expect to occasionally have to say "I don't know" or "I don't recall at the moment," as being very much preferred over guessing or dodging
the question. When time is growing short it is well to indicate that
there is time remaining for only one or two more questions,
instead of closing abruptly.

5-8. LETTERS OF APPLICATION. The letter of
application on the following page is a composite of typical (exaggerated in some instances) phrases and sentences received in actual
letters and in student assignments. Sections of this letter have
been numbered to correspond to the commentary.

Letter of Application
(Sample for Criticism)

①   Mr. John Doe
        33 W. 46 Street
        B_____, C_____

Professor _____
University of _____
C_____, M_____

②   My Dear Professor:

③   I understand that you have an opening for a young instructor in the Civil Engineering Department. ④ I believe that I am the man for this place and wish to make application for it.

⑤   My record follows:

⑥   I have B.S. and M.S. degrees from ———, the best engineering school in America. ⑦ I took a one year training course with ABC steel corporation and did excellent work in structural design which qualifies me as an instructor in structural design.

⑧   I have been an Instructor at ——— University for one year, but desire to make a change as there is no future to the position and those now in charge are twenty years behind the times.

⑨   For references you can contact the engineering department at ABC. Please do not write to the ——— University officials where I am presently teaching.

⑩   I wish to say that I have no bad habits that is I do not swear, drink, or use tobacco in any form. I strongly believe that one should be dependable and energetic in any job they tackle and I can assure you that you will find that I display these characteristics.

⑪   I am married and have one of the finest girls for my wife. She is a good scout and takes an active part in social affairs.

⑫   I will be able to visit your campus next month, if you think an interview is necessary and you can arrange to reimburse me for my expenses.

⑬   Yours for improvement in teaching,

_____

⑭   P. S. Salary expected to be such that I could save at least one-fifth above all expenses.

Commentary:

① Standard letter heading typed form should not include name of writer (normally, only included at bottom in closing). Date should be included below the address.

② Salutation is too familiar for a letter of this type.

③ The source of knowledge of the opening (e.g., advertisement, individual, etc.) should be indicated. Otherwise, it is best to apply for a "possible opening."

④ The reader of the letter is not at all likely to appreciate having the applicant decide who is the man for the job. Statements indicating characteristics of brashness and ego sometimes are confused with an attempt to display self-confidence. Whereas there is desirability in demonstrating a "quiet self-confidence" it must be done very delicately and skillfully; and it is best left for an interview, not the letter of application. "Quiet self-confidence" is the Golden Mean between excessive ego and humility; and, as it is most difficult to strike the Golden Mean, it is usually best to err on the side of humility. It is well to use the engineering approach of letting the facts speak for themselves.

⑤ Whereas many individuals seem to prefer to include their record in the body of a letter of application, the author is strongly of the opinion it is best to refer to an enclosure of one's personal data (see §5-9 on Personal Resumé) written in the third person. Excessive use of the personal pronoun "I" is difficult to avoid if one's record is included in the body of the letter. A tabular form, as suggested, also makes the data easier to follow and better for later reference.

⑥ Broad, unqualified ranking of institutions or individuals is a dangerous practice. Rankings, when existing, are continually changing; and in most instances such rankings are not objective or officially recognized. For example, there is no official numerical over-all ranking of engineering schools; yet, as in this letter, one seems to find graduates from a hundred different institutions all considering themselves graduates of one of the top ten institutions. Whereas one should be proud of his own institution, it is not wise to make judgments which cannot readily be substantiated and are likely to be both controversial and insulting if the prospective employer's background is different.

⑦ Here again phrases such as "excellent work" and "qualifies me" are generally going to be judged as prejudiced self-opinions. The employer will wish to form his own opinions from the facts, and possibly from statements given by previous employers and other references.

⑧ It has been suggested that if one cannot speak well of others involved in our personal relations, it ordinarily is best to say nothing. The prospective employer cannot help wondering as to what will be said about his organization if and when the applicant were to leave the new position. The reason for desiring a change can generally be better stated positively, e.g., "to obtain broader experience."

⑨ ABC Steel Corporation's engineering department may consist of several hundred employees, including secretarial and possibly janitorial staff—specific individuals should be indicated as references.

⑩ It should be obvious that it is best not to volunteer information about one's personal habits or characteristics such as: "I am subject to occasional attacks of dandruff and athlete's foot." Overanxiety to create a good impression can lead to statements as in the sample letter; or conversely, overanxiety to be honest and not misrepresent themselves cause some to feel obligated to point out or emphasize their personal failings (e.g., "I have not had much experience"). All people have both strong points and failings which the prospective employer will attempt to determine for himself from a personal resumé, references, and possibly directed questions.

⑪ It is also best not to volunteer information about one's family. If the employer is concerned, he will ask.

⑫ A vacation can be combined with an interview visit (at one's own expense); or wait for an invitation. Also it is best to avoid absolute phrases such as "always," "never"—"I will be able" is similar in that it infers a certainty to an indefinite future (e.g., he might not be alive next month). In speaking of the future it is preferable to use typically: "I expect to be," "I anticipate," "I hope."

⑬ The closing of a formal letter is best left simple (e.g., sincerely yours, yours truly) without such inept attempts at cleverness.

⑭ Discussion of salary is a delicate matter best left to be initiated by the employer. It is particularly inappropriate in the first correspondence from the applicant.

A letter of application can sometimes, in and of itself, obtain a job for the writer. However, this is likely to happen only when the employer is having considerable difficulty in filling vacancies, and then usually the positions will tend to be at the lower levels. More typically, a letter of application serves primarily to create enough interest so that the employer will desire to bring in the applicant for an interview.

Following the above philosophy a letter of application should be concise and objective. Particular attention should be paid to spelling, both of oneself and the typist; the one who signs the letter is ultimately responsible for its contents. The previous composite letter has been rewritten below. This letter covers sequentially five points, which should be included in most letters of application. These points are listed below the letter.

33 W. 46 Street
B_____, C_____
May 15, 19__

Professor _____
School of Engineering
University of _____
C_____, M_____

Dear Professor _____:

①   In reply to your advertisement in the April issue of the Journal of Engineering Education I wish to present this application for a position as an instructor in your Civil Engineering Department,
② preferably beginning this coming Fall semester.
③   My previous contacts and experience in education have interested me in a career in college teaching; and I would hope to be able to combine both classroom teaching duties and research activities. Ever since my first, and most pleasant, period of residence in your community I have looked forward to returning and settling there. For this reason I am particularly desirous of obtaining a position on your faculty.
④   Enclosed herewith is a copy of my personal resumé for your consideration. I shall be pleased to furnish any additional informa-
⑤ tion at your request. I also expect to be visiting near the campus between June 3 and June 10; and I could be available for an interview, at your convenience, during this period.

Sincerely yours,

_____
John Doe

① Indicate the position applied for, and source of information about this position. If no information is available, apply for a possible opening.
② Indicate when available to accept the position.
③ Give brief factual and sincere reasons why employment is desired

with the specific organization and in the specific position. These reasons may include geographical location, specialized type of work offered, etc.

④ Indicate enclosure of personal resumé.

⑤ Indicate when and where available for an interview, if one can be available at his own expense.

5-9. THE PERSONAL RESUMÉ. The personal resumé should be an objective summary of information which would be of interest or needed when applying for employment, admission to organizations, engineering registration, etc. Some individuals choose to prepare a considerable number of copies of their personal resumé in some duplicator process; however, it is strongly recommended that one not prepare any more copies than are needed for immediate use. Preparation of a good personal resumé requires some skill; it is assumed that, as time goes on, this skill as well as one's qualifications would improve. If old copies of a personal resumé are still available, the natural laziness of most people will create a strong tendency to just use the old one instead of taking the time to prepare a new and better resumé. It is also doubtful that any one form of resumé can well serve many different applications. That is, the well prepared resumé is concisely pointed for its specific application; and therefore each specific application can be best served by a uniquely prepared resumé which emphasizes the qualifications most pertinent to that application.

It is suggested that primary attention be given to the preparation of a *master copy* of the personal resumé from which reference data may be extracted for completion of application forms or for preparation of a more concise resumé needed for a specific purpose. This master copy should be arranged in a form which will readily allow additions to bring it up to date; and it might well be kept with other important papers such as birth certificate, college transcript, automobile title, insurance policies, etc. A suggested form, and commentary thereon, for a master copy of a personal resumé is shown.

MASTER COPY
PERSONAL RESUMÉ

① Name: _____   ② Present Address: _____
   Citizenship: _____   Permanent Address: _____
   Birthdate: _____   Addresses for last 15 years (dates):
   Height: ____ Weight: _____   _____
   Social Security No.: _____   _____
   Marital Status: _____
   Military status: _____   Languages read or spoken: ___
③ Education:

School & Location	Attendance Dates	Diplomas or Degrees

④ Experience:
   Employer: _____
   Title & Duties: _____

   Dates: _____ Final Salary: _____
   Immediate Supervisor: _____

   Reason for Leaving: _____

   Employer: _____
   Title & Duties: _____

   Dates: _____ ....
⑤ Memberships (include offices held and dates): _____

   Honors and Awards: _____
⑥ Hobbies: _____
⑦ Technical Papers: _____
⑧ References (at least 5):

Name (known since)	Address	Occupation

Commentary:

① This is vital data that should probably be included in all specific resumés prepared.

② The college student who is about to graduate should show both his temporary college address and a more permanent address (e.g., that of one's parents) where correspondence can be sent for forwarding. Some application forms (e.g., those of government agencies where security checks are desired) require all addresses for the last 15 years. This information is sometimes most difficult to recall. If one starts now to record past addresses and then adds each change of address to the master copy as it occurs, completion of such forms becomes relatively simple—this latter type of information ordinarily need not be volunteered and should be omitted from a personal resumé initiated by the applicant.

③ It is suggested that all schools attended including all elementary schools, high schools, colleges, service schools, short courses, formal educational conferences, etc., be listed on the master copy. Ordinarily only the high school and subsequent education would be of interest to an employer. However, if elementary school attendance was the only period of residence in the geographical region in which the prospective employer is located, it would be well to list such schooling as objective evidence of a degree of familiarity with the region. Most employers recognize that an individual who chooses a geographical region based upon actual experience is a better risk, in terms of being satisfied with existing conditions, than an individual who may be coming in new to the region with many misconceptions. Most students have difficulty with the manner of presentation of their college education, just prior to graduation, on a letter of resumé. Good engineering practice would not assume a certainty (even for the honor student) for an indefinite future; and therefore a commonly used statement such as "I will be graduated in June 1966" or a listing "B.S. June 1966" (prior to such graduation) is preferably replaced by a listing "B.S. (Candidate) June 1966."

④ The most important and difficult part of the resumé to present properly is one's experience record. The young graduate, with relatively little experience, should generally list all experience including part-time and summer jobs, at least for the first few years after graduation. Even experience which is not related to engineering is of interest to most employers as some evidence of an ability to work with others and of an appreciation of the general obligations of employee to employer—all too often the graduate who has never worked before tends to believe that one should be paid if he is on the employer's premises (e.g., he cannot go hunting and fishing) regardless of the amount of work accomplished. Experience should preferably be listed chronologically to show an *ascending* development.

The master copy should include under title and duties a complete record of one's specific assignments (e.g., right-of-way design on the southern leg of the Sunshine State Parkway, landing gear design on the Thunderjet plane, design of guidance components of the Atlas missile, etc.). Mere listings of employers' names and titles of positions often do not reflect the significant aspects of one's experience. For example a Civil Engineering student merely listed under "experience" that he worked 2 years for the Jones Landscaping Company and served as a sergeant for 3 years in the Signal Corps. One might thereby obtain the impression that his time was respectively spent in mowing grass and operating a telegraph key—neither of which would be particularly significant for Civil Engineering employment. However, further inquiry about his duties brought out the omitted facts that with the landscape company he had obtained considerable experience with heavy equipment including bulldozers and cranes; and in the Signal Corps most of his work had been in demolitions where he had become quite expert in the handling and use of explosives. The desired conciseness of a specific resumé would generally preclude the listing of all one's specific assignments recorded in the master copy; but here one may skillfully select representative examples of one's assignments which would best point toward the particular application.

A statement of the reasons for leaving each previous employment probably should not be volunteered in a specific resumé; however, such statements are frequently requested by employers and therefore it is desirable to have these reasons stated in the master copy with due prior consideration. For example, a negatively stated reason for leaving (e.g., the firm was twenty years behind the times) would be better stated positively (e.g., to obtain broader experience).

⑤ Memberships, honors and awards are an indicator that the prospective employee may be willing to do more than the bare minimum requirements of the job. Certainly every engineer who is aware of his responsibilities beyond the self should belong to at least one professional organization.

⑥ All other things being equal, if an applicant happens to have the same hobby as the employer, (e.g., philately or astronomy), he is quite likely to receive some preferential consideration. Organizational teams in bowling, softball, etc., are often sources of considerable interest and pride, and new employees with such aptitudes may here again receive preferential consideration. The listings of one's hobbies, except for a few having poor connotation (e.g., poker, pool), will not hurt one's application and may often strike a responsive chord.

⑦ Technical papers which have been published or presented at a formal professional meeting are important objective evidence of significant contribution to the profession and to one's own experience. It is well to have a heading and space allocation on the master copy of one's resumé as a continual reminder of the need to fulfill this important obligation of making such contributions to the profession. A specific resumé should necessarily omit this heading until one or more papers have been contributed.

⑧ The master copy might well include current addresses of a wide scope of references including professional, faculty, close friends, and family physician and minister. It should be recognized, while making applications as a senior student, that one's classmates will also soon be in professional practice and may serve as very appropriate references both in the near future and at the present. It is both proper courtesy toward the individual listed as a reference, and to one's own interests, to inform him of significant new occurrences in one's activities. If one has not been in recent contact with someone being listed as a reference, it may be appropriate to bring him up to date by forwarding a copy of a recent personal resumé.

5-10. THE JOB INTERVIEW. Both the applicant and the employer (who today often averages several thousands of dollars in costs for each professional employee recruited) have to make rather important decisions based upon the relatively few minutes of mutual experience in a job interview. The importance of this experience justifies thorough preparation, including the prior development of skill in handling oneself during an interview. Whereas suggestions about interviews, as indicated in the following paragraphs, may be helpful, skill in interviewing is best achieved thru experience in actual interviews. Recruitment visits are held frequently at most college campuses offering a convenient means of obtaining a broad experience in interviewing, as well as a better perspective of job opportunities; thus making it less likely for one to be thinking the grass is greener elsewhere shortly after accepting employment.

Prior preparations for an interview might well include the following:

1. Have in mind what information you desire to know about the prospective employer. Time can be saved during the interview, and it will usually make a good impression, if one takes the trouble to ascertain as much as possible about the employer, prior to the interview. Information about the larger corporations is usually available from such sources as University Placement Centers, Manufacturers' Directories, stock brokers, Chambers of Commerce, and faculty. Some of the information one might wish to ascertain, either prior to or during the interview, includes:

   a) Geographical location of the firm;
   b) Status of the firm;
   c) Opportunities for continuing education (e.g., graduate studies, In-service training);
   d) Specific assignment (e.g., specialized or broad experience, qualifying for professional registration minimum experience, function, etc.);
   e) Qualifications of immediate supervisors (e.g., registered engineers, nationally known, etc.);
   f) Opportunities for contacts outside the organization (e.g., attendance at national conventions, meeting the public, etc.);
   g) Length of work week (regularity of hours, overtime, flexibility in restitution for time-off, etc.);
   h) Salary and opportunities for advancement—salary discussions are delicate matters and best left to the initiative of the employer, the applicant preferably being in a position of either accepting or rejecting an offer.
   i) Fringe Benefits (e.g., vacation, sick leave, insurance, tenure, and retirement benefits)—Fringe benefits, as is salary, are delicate matters to discuss. For example, a recruiter commented to the author: "This student was applying for what would have been the first significant job he ever held, and all he seemed

concerned about was how much and when he could start receiving retirement benefits."

2. Have available a copy of one's personal resumé (if it, or an application form, has not been submitted previously) and samples of work. Availability of the personal resumé during the interview makes for a more efficient use of the time to go into depth, and also tends to reduce the probable use of the personal pronoun "I" by the applicant. Samples of work should be presented if requested, or held in reserve for an appropriate time in the interview. Samples of work to be presented should be chosen to demonstrate ability to perform: clear, neat, well-organized work; original work; or major complex projects.

3. Over-all appearance should be checked. The prospective employer is quite certain to believe the interview is important enough for the applicant to take the trouble to put forth his best countenance. A conservative business suit should be worn—"Joe College" attire, or the latest extreme in fashion, is likely to indicate unconcern or ostentation.

4. If possible, obtain an introduction by others who are known to the prospective employer. The prospective employer is likely to report back, and therefore will tend to weigh more carefully the decision about employment.

5. Arrive early for the interview—it is better for you to wait than the prospective employer.

During the interview itself the following factors might be considered, sequentially:

1. *Handshake:* A limp fish handshake immediately tends to give the impression of a weak, ineffective personality. Almost everyone can quickly and easily, through practice, develop a firm handshake. If one is not sure of his handshake, it would be well to have a room-mate or friend evaluate it and offer practice, if needed.

2. *Depository:* The prospective employer is not at all likely to

appreciate the applicant requisitioning the top of his desk for depositing such articles as a hat, samples of work, etc. These should be kept on one's lap or placed on a distant chair, or other appropriate place.

3. *Smoking and gum-chewing*: The applicant offering gum or a cigarette to the prospective employer would immediately symbolize brazenness and untoward familiarity. In accepting an offered cigarette, the applicant's smoking habits are likely to create an impression of unconcern and inattentiveness. Refraining from smoking is unlikely to hurt one's chances at any time; whereas smoking is unlikely to ever help and may often injure one's chances.

4. *Conversation*: There is no stereotyped manner in which interviewers attempt to evaluate an applicant. Some interviewers prefer to force the applicant to initiate all the conversation by maintaining an initial silence and answering all questions essentially with a clipped yes or no. Other interviewers may ask leading questions such as "Why do you want the job?," "How did you happen to study engineering?," "What types of books (other than texts) have you read?," "What is your major weakness?," or "What kind of people rub you the wrong way?" The interviewer may attempt to see how easily one is goaded to anger, how frequently one drifts off into long-winded monologues about irrelevant matters, or if one is a chronic malcontent. Whereas one should not speak in a derogatory manner about others, many interviewers like to see an applicant who will take a definite considered stand against or for an issue or principle. The ability to handle the conversation well during an interview can best be developed by sufficient experience in interviews.

5. *Signals of Termination:* Some applicants become so carried away with the conversation about themselves that they fail to note that the interviewer has been impatiently trying to terminate the interview as may be signaled by looking at his watch, letting the conversation lag, or gathering

papers. Some individuals also seem to be unable to complete their good-byes, lingering on and on at the verge of an exit. The interviewer would prefer not to have bluntly to push the applicant out the door; and the applicant should remain alert to recognize promptly subtle signals of a termination of the interview, which must come.

6. *Leave with Something Positive:* It should generally be possible to leave the interview with some positive knowledge of the future. Ideally, one might leave with an offer of employment; however, one should at least be able to find out approximately when a decision will be made and how the applicant will be informed of the decision. The applicant also can and should indicate, if after due consideration during the interview, that he has become convinced of the advantages of employment with the firm and that he would welcome an offer—or that the firm would be his first choice. All other things being equal, the employer will usually prefer to make an offer to an applicant who has shown positive interest and enthusiasm, before considering an applicant who has left with a neutral or negative attitude.

ASSIGNMENTS

5.1. Determine where the following periodicals are indexed or abstracted:

 a) Rubber Chemistry and Technology
 b) Nondestructive Testing
 c) Electrical Manufacturing
 d) Journal of Chromatography
 e) Society of Glass Technology-Journal

5.2. List 3 bibliographical items related to each of any 5 of the following topics obtained from (list index for each): (A) Periodical index (B) Government document index (C) Bibliography of bibliographies (D) Doctoral dissertation index (E) Patent index (F) Specification index:

a) Wood Preservatives   e) Aluminum Alloys
b) Tubes and Pipe   f) Lubricants
c) Plastics   g) Fire-alarm systems
d) Cement   h) Insulation

5.3. Given the following titles of broad subjects for a possible 10-page article, list three closely related titles each of which successively narrows the scope of the given topic (see page 172 for example):

a) Aluminum   d) Operations research
b) Solid state electronics   e) Servomechanisms
c) Gas dynamics   f) Electrochemistry

5.4. Prepare an abstract (not to exceed 5 per cent of the length of the original) of a specific periodical article or chapter of a textbook.

5.5. For the standards listed below:
a) Prepare a preliminary outline and partial bibliography for a paper and speech.
b) Prepare a paper and speech.

Standards for Engineering Papers

(A) Written papers are to be a minimum length of 10 double-spaced typed pages ($8\frac{1}{2} \times 11$ inches with approximate margins of $1\frac{1}{4}$ inches at top, $1\frac{1}{2}$ inches at left, 1 inch at bottom and $\frac{3}{4}$ inch at right). Oral presentation to take 15 to 20 minutes plus a 3 to 5 minute discussion (defense) period.

(B) Subjects are to be narrow in scope and are *not* to cover material that is ordinarily included in the engineering curriculum. Suggested sources of topics are: potential areas of specialization in a future job, current controversies, topics related to unusual personal experiences or hobbies, and current research (particularly on campus). Consideration should be given to appropriateness of the topic as an entry in local or national contests.

(C) Papers are to include all of the parts (e.g., abstract,

bibliography) listed in § 5-6, except possibly an appendix. The bibliography should be listed in proper form; and sources should include some search through periodical indexes. The use of sub-topic headings should be considered.

(D) Both written and oral presentations are to be in third person. Absolute and personal derogatory or laudatory statements should be avoided.

(E) Sketches and charts shall be in accordance with drawing standards.

(F) Oral presentation shall be primarily extemporaneous (preferably using notes on 3×5-inch cards). Courtesy dictates that the presentation be timed beforehand to keep within the time allocated. Arrangements for visual aids, if needed, should also be made beforehand (when blackboard sketches require more than 15 to 20 seconds to draw they should be completed prior to the start of the class period or meeting).

(G) Papers are to be evaluated primarily upon organization of the topic, clarity of expression, grammatical construction, spelling, and conformity with the above standards. Particular note should be made that the proof-reading of the typing is a most important responsibility of the author.

5.6.   Assume (and indicate) a set of circumstances and write:

a) A letter of application;

b) A letter of acceptance of a job offer;

c) A letter rejecting a job offer;

d) A letter offering employment to an applicant for an engineering position;

e) An advertisement for engineering help wanted;

f) A news release to accompany introduction of a new product;

g) An instruction manual or bulletin;

h) A welcome address;

i) A farewell address;

j) An acceptance speech;

k) An address commemorating an event.

5.7.   Prepare a master copy of a personal resumé.

5.8. Write a report on an actual job interview. Include information about the position which would be of probable interest to others seeking similar employment, and also an analysis of particular incidents which may have left very favorable or unfavorable impressions.

BIBLIOGRAPHY

(1) HICKS, TYLER G. *Writing for Engineering and Science.* New York: McGraw-Hill Book Company, Inc., 1961, 298 pp.
(2) KIERZEK, J. M. and GIBSON, WALKER. *The Macmillan Handbook of English.* 4th edition; New York. The Macmillan Company, 1960. 489 pp.
(3) *A Manual of Style.* 11th ed.; Chicago: University of Chicago Press, 1949. 534 pp.

SUGGESTED ADDITIONAL READING

GILMAN, W. E., *et al. The Fundamentals of Speaking.* New York: The Macmillan Company, 1951. 608 pp.
HARWELL, GEORGE. *Technical Communication.* New York: The Macmillan Company, 1960. 332 pp.
RHODES, FRED H. *Technical Report Writing.* New York: McGraw-Hill Book Company, Inc., 1961. 168 pp.
SIMMONS, HARRY. *Executive Public Speaking Techniques.* New York: Chilton Company, 1959. 231 pp.

CHAPTER 6

Continuation of Education

6-1. LIFELONG LEARNING. Completion of the requirements for a degree may signify the end of classroom instruction, but education should end only with life. The young graduate normally has available a considerable amount of leisure time, in comparison to his period of residence in the engineering school. It is well to start early to plan to use this newly found leisure time effectively, before the leisure time gradually seems to disappear through dissipating habits. Whereas many may have the opportunity to continue after the Bachelor's degree in graduate studies or an organizational training program, after completion of graduate studies or a training program the same problem exists of using one's leisure time effectively for continuing self study.

Continuous advances in science and technology bringing new materials, methods, processes, and problems creates demands for never ending study and learning. If the average engineer did no studying and learning after obtaining the experience required for registration, he would become obsolete in a relatively few years. This obsolescence is to be expected even after obtaining the maximum graduate degree, if studying is not continued. Outside of the technical areas, lifelong learning is necessary for a fuller appreciation and enjoyment of human existence.

Regular reading of books and periodicals in both technical and cultural areas should be started immediately, while one is still in the habit of studying. Supplementing self study, one can regularly receive enrichment through activities in professional and civic societies, and attendance at specialized technical programs such as short courses, symposiums, and conferences.

6-2. GRADUATE STUDY OPPORTUNITIES AND ADVANTAGES. The need and importance of advanced formal studies beyond the bachelor's degree is being recognized by increasing numbers of engineering students. At this writing (as reported by the U. S. Department of Health, Education & Welfare, Office of Education) the numbers of students receiving bachelor's degrees in engineering has been declining for five consecutive years, while the number of masters' degrees in engineering is up 9 per cent over the previous year and the number of doctor's degrees in engineering is up 28 per cent over the previous year. Presently, the annual number of masters' degrees in engineering represents over 25 per cent of the number receiving bachelor's degrees in engineering; and about 14 per cent of those receiving masters' degrees continue on to complete the doctorate, with both percentages rising rapidly.

Graduate study in most areas of engineering rests upon a firm prerequisite basis in undergraduate engineering studies differing from other professions such as law and medicine where the primary professional education follows an undergraduate program of a more general nature. Whereas professional advancement in engineering can be continued readily after the undergraduate degree solely by organizational training programs and/or self-study, there are considerable advantages to advanced studies in a formal graduate program. The general advantages of formal graduate studies include: the availability of larger libraries and specialized laboratories, the opportunity to work closely with outstanding scholars in one's field of interest, the additional stimulation of contact with fellow students from many different institutions and organizations, and finally the international recognition received for one's efforts and accomplishments upon the award of the master's and doctor's degrees. Most engineering positions involving the functions of teaching and research will require advanced degrees—and ever more insistently, the maximum degree.

If one is qualified and plans to undertake graduate studies, there are the further decisions of whether these studies should be done on a full-time or part-time basis and also whether they should be taken immediately after completion of the bachelor's degree or after several years experience have been obtained. The arguments for waiting some time before entering graduate school are that one might thereby, from direct experience, know better which is the preferred area of specialization and that one can come back refreshed and recuperated from a strenuous 4 or 5 year period of study for the bachelor's degree. On the other hand, one may wait too long and get out of the habit of studying and forget many broad fundamentals, particularly advanced mathematics and theoretical principles, not used in one's specific employment. As a substitute, summer employment can be used to supplement the undergraduate experience in helping to choose an area of specialization for graduate study. The most difficult problem, particularly if one is married, is the adjustment downward in the standard of living while gainfully employed to that usually necessitated by full-time graduate studies. Also, there may often be losses in seniority and retirement benefits incurred by the interruption and/or change in employment.

Graduate study in full-time residence normally involves some temporary financial sacrifices, in comparison with what one may have been or could be earning. Balanced against this sacrifice are the statistics of potential gain in life-time earnings. At present the median earnings of engineers with master's degrees is about 10 to 20 per cent (depending upon years since graduation) higher than those with only bachelor's degrees. Engineers with doctor's degrees have a 25 to 60 per cent greater median income, in comparison with those having only the bachelor's degree.

Many opportunities are available to undertake graduate studies on a part-time basis while employed in industry. Major advantages of this type of graduate study are the easing of the financial burden and the possibility of fitting graduate studies more closely to the needs of one's major employment interest. Major disadvantages of part-time graduate studies are the loss of close continuous contact between faculty and student which creates much of the unique climate of the graduate school, division of interests and time usually resulting in lesser efforts and accomplishment, and the extended time required for the degree. If the time is dragged out too long, one's thesis or dissertation supervisor may accept another position, retire or die; and it may be necessary to find and start anew on a project which another faculty member is willing to supervise. Also, the general requirements for recency of credit, typically being that work taken more than 5 to 8 years prior is not acceptable for a degree, may become a serious handicap.

Opportunities for part-time graduate studies may range from that of mere availability of a nearby graduate school offering classes after normal working hours, to those where the employer makes considerable contributions of both time and financial resources. A number of graduate-cooperative programs are available; these tend to differ from the typical undergraduate alternating periods of work and study in that they usually involve employment (and pay) for fractional parts of each week, with the remainder of the week devoted to studies. Other opportunities involve tuition grants or refunds for successful completion of graduate work which is taken on the employee's own time after working hours. Some employers give both tuition reimbursements and released company time for graduate studies; and amongst the finest of opportunities may be found grants of a paid leave of absence for full-time graduate study, after a period of creditable employment (which may include some successful part-time graduate studies).

6-3. FINANCIAL AID FOR GRADUATE STUDY IN RESIDENCE.
At present, and for the foreseeable future, there appears to be significant financial aid available for almost every well-qualified applicant for graduate study in engineering. This may not be true for any one graduate school in any one year; but if a well-qualified student submits applications to a reasonable number of different schools, he generally may

expect to receive one or more offers of financial aid. Many competitions for financial aid have closing dates which are quite early. Applications should be going out by November (preferably in September or October) of the year prior to the Fall semester when studies are to begin.

The general categories of financial aid for study in residence include the following:

(a) Fellowships—The Fellowship grant usually requires no services in return and is usually exempt from income taxes. Some Fellowships include tuition and fee exemptions, some do not. A full course of study is usually required. Grants are usually for increasing amounts for study respectively for the Master's degree, Doctor's degree, and Post-Doctoral work. Post-Doctoral work involves study and research, for its own sake, and is most frequently done at a different institution from that in which the degree work is completed.

(b) Assistantships—Assistantships are aid given in return for part-time employment in residence. Employment may be as a research assistant, grading papers, undergraduate laboratory instructor, and in some instances having full responsibility for teaching sections of elementary courses. Usually a full load of studies cannot be carried and the length of time for the degree is therefore extended. Assistantship salaries are currently subject to income tax; tuition and fees may or may not be exempted. A research assistant may be able to use, advantageously, his research assignment as a thesis topic. A teaching assistantship affords the opportunity to judge if one wishes a career in the teaching field.

(c) Scholarships—Graduate scholarships are usually smaller in amounts than either the Fellowship or Assistantship. They generally include only tuition and fees and require no work in return. Scholarships are normally exempt from Federal Income Tax.

(d) Loans—The terms and amounts of available loans vary considerably. A number of loans are available which may be forgiveable upon completion of a specified period and type of employment, after graduation, such as teaching or with a specific employer or in a specific geographical area.

Further details relative to financial aid may be obtained from the references listed in Table 5-1 on page 164, and from direct inquiries to the institutions.

6-4. SELECTION OF AND ADMISSION TO GRADUATE SCHOOL.

The best advice about selection of and admission to a graduate school can be expected from some one who is familiar with the individual's interests and abilities and also the graduate schools being considered. The bulletin of one's own undergraduate school can be used to determine the source of the degrees of the faculty and thereby to locate individuals who can give first-hand information about many graduate schools. This personal information is best checked against recent bulletins of the graduate school and by correspondence or visitation as changes, including faculty turnover, are taking place rapidly. If one wants to work under a particular member of the graduate faculty, it is well to check if he can take any more students, is away on leave, etc. It is usually recommended that the Master's, or at least the Doctor's degree, be taken at an institution different from the Bachelor's in order to give access to a broader range of ideas and approaches to one's major subject.

Most graduate schools will accept the Bachelor's degree in the same discipline from an accredited school, even if the course work is somewhat different from their own Bachelor's degree requirements. Many graduate schools will also readily allow changing of major (e.g., from a B.S. in Mechanical Engineering to a M.S. in Civil Engineering) if the prerequisites to the area of graduate specialization have been completed. On the other hand, a few graduate schools have insisted upon undergraduate deficiency courses being taken wherever the Bachelor's degree differs from their own requirements, even in the same discipline. It is well to have a clear cut understanding about any possible undergraduate deficiencies prior to entrance to the graduate school.

Admission to graduate school is usually based primarily upon scholastic average and recommendations; and sometimes job experience and score on the Graduate Record Examination are weighed. A scholastic average in the upper 25 per cent and satisfactory recommendations will usually obtain regular admission. Lower over-all averages may be compensated by a record showing progressive improvement in the average in the later years, or by a higher average in the major field. A high score on the Graduate Record Examination, consisting of area and aptitude tests taken by applicants in all disciplines and an advanced test which is the same for all engineering disciplines, may sometimes be used to compensate for a relatively low scholastic average. Some graduate schools ask the applicant to have letters of recommendation forwarded; other schools ask only for names of references whom they may contact. Both letters of recommendation and transcripts of grades should be sent directly to the graduate school and not transmitted by the applicant. Transcripts, particularly, are not accepted if handled at any time by the applicant.

In some instances superior undergraduates, having only a relatively few required courses in their last semester or quarter, may be permitted to take some courses for graduate credit. Many graduate schools will allow 6 to 8 semester credits for graduate work to be transferred for the Master's degree. The Master's degree normally will transfer as one year of work toward the Doctorate; and some schools will accept up to 2 years of transferred graduate work for the Doctorate.

6-5. GRADUATE DEGREE REQUIREMENTS.
The requirements and curriculum for graduate students will, to a large extent, vary with the individuals' needs and interests as evaluated by the student and an advisory committee. Although there is some general agreement on the nominal amount of time

required to complete the various graduate degrees, considerable variability and flexibility in approach, credit hours, and steps to completion have been the trend.

Two designations for Master's degrees are generally found: The Master of Science in a designated field, and the Master of Engineering in a designated field. The Master of Science degree is usually administered under the Graduate School, engineering being administered along with other disciplines such as mathematics, physics, history, etc. The Master of Engineering degree usually is administered solely under the School or College of Engineering and tends to be more professionally oriented with course work, reports, or an individual project often being substituted for a thesis. Most engineering schools offer either the Master of Science or Master of Engineering; and occasionally both degrees are offered. The minimum time requirement for completion of the Master's degree is one academic year. Credit hour requirements approximate 30 semester hours with an average grade of B, with the thesis making up from 3 to 8 hours of the total. A greater number of credit hours is usually required for the non-thesis option, where such an option exists. Generally students working for the Master's degree on an assistantship will require 2 years for completion.

The Doctoral degree usually involves a minimum of three years work beyond the Bachelor's degree, with the Master's degree generally being counted as part of the three years work. It is also possible to work directly for the Doctorate without obtaining the Master's degree. The equivalent of two of the three years are generally devoted to formal course work and the last year to research related to the dissertation. The median number of years between completion of the Bachelor's and Doctoral degrees has been 4.3 years. Three types of Doctoral degree in engineering are generally available: The Doctor of Philosophy (Ph.D.), the Doctor of Science (Sc.D.), and the Doctor of Engineering (D.Eng.). The Doctor of Philosophy degree is usually administered by the Graduate School, while the Doctor of Science and Doctor of Engineering are more often administered by the School or College of Engineering. The Sc.D and D.Eng. degrees often tend to be more professionally oriented to design instead of research and also usually have lesser requirements in the knowledge of foreign languages.

Professional degrees typically designated as Civil Engineer (C.E.) Electrical Engineer (E.E.), or Mechanical Engineer (M.E.) have in the past traditionally been given as non-resident degrees to graduates of their own School or College. The requirements generally have been satisfactory evidence of professional engineering experience of creditable quality over a period of from 4 to 6 years, a thesis (prior publications may be accepted) as further evidence of professional attainment, and an examination on the thesis. More recently the trend has been to make the Professional Degree one with resident course work requirements—in some instances closely approximating the requirements for the Master of Engineering, and being offered instead of the Master of Engineering. In some instances the resident Professional Degree requires fewer credit hours and a lower grade average than the Master's degree. In other instances Professional registration is required in addition to the course work and thesis; and in some instances the requirements are such that the degree is considered to be attainable only after completion of the Master's degree, as a degree intermediate between the Master's and Doctoral degree.

The graduate course work is generally classified as being in a major field and in minor fields. The major field usually involves work in a single department; however, it may also include courses which are cross-listed in two or more departments, and recently a number of schools are encouraging an integrated interdisciplinary program including courses in a number of departments to make up an *area major*. The minor commonly refers to work done in departments other than that of the major department. For the Master's degree requirements are sometimes stated: that at least two-thirds of the work shall be in the major (not specifying the amount in the minor), and sometimes stated: that at least one-third of the course work shall be in the minor. For the Doctoral degree 2 minors are often required, the minor comprising the equivalent of about one full semester of work. Where an area major is undertaken, the major-minor categories are usually eliminated.

The Doctoral dissertation is generally expected to demonstrate the ability to do an original, independent investigation which makes a significant contribution to knowledge. The dissertation should also demonstrate a mastery of the sources of information about the subject and be presented with satisfactory literary skill, including material worthy of publication. The priority of possible publication should be watched as many schools will not accept a dissertation if it is published prior to approval by the school. One study on the length of engineering Ph.D. dissertations showed a median number of pages of 136, a total range of 31 to 617 pages, with the middle half ranging between 102 to 185 pages. There is presently considerable sentiment for dissertations being written in a shorter form, as a manuscript submitted for publication in a professional journal. An outline, sample chapter or chapters, and a partial bibliography are usually submitted by the student in requesting approval of the subject matter of the dissertation. In selecting a dissertation topic, the student should weigh carefully the probability of completion within a reasonable length of time. For example, a search for a device which eliminates gravitational effects might be a most worthy endeavor; but there is an exceedingly high probability that one could work a lifetime and not come forth with an acceptable solution. It is preferable to pick a subject for which either positive or negative results are acceptable. Negative findings which narrow the field of possibilities of an unknown also contribute to the convergence upon the truth.

Time being shorter, the Master's thesis research will necessarily be smaller in scope than the research required for the Ph. D. dissertation. Also, instead of being based on research resulting in an original significant contribution to knowledge, the Master's thesis may be accepted if it is considered to be a contribution to the education of the candidate. Included amongst acceptable Master's thesis, in addition to those based on actual research performance, have been: projects intended to *develop* research ability; projects involving a practical engineering problem solved in a novel manner; a graduated series of projects culminating in an independent effort; and reports on topics which include a critical interpretation of the literature in the field.

Traditionally, a knowledge of foreign languages has been a partial requirement for graduate degrees. This has been justified as being a necessary tool for research, the mark of an educated or cultured man, and also as an important disciplinary hurdle for the scholar. At present foreign languages are rather rarely required for the Master's degree in the engineering fields; however, a reading knowledge of two languages, usually French and German, are typically a partial requirement for the Ph. D. Russian and other languages have been increasingly accepted instead of French or German, while for foreign students English is sometimes accepted for one language. Some schools have indicated a preference for having one language known thoroughly, and used in the dissertation, instead of having a mediocre reading knowledge of two languages. Other schools have allowed the replacement for one language by statistics, computer technology, or other special research techniques. Still other schools now require, primarily for the D. Eng. or Sc. D., only one language; and in some instances no foreign languages are required.

Comprehensive oral and written examinations are generally required for both the Master's and Doctoral degrees. These examinations may be given prior to admission to candidacy or after completion of all course work, or both. Admission to candidacy for a degree is a separate formal step from admission to the graduate school. Purposes of the formal step of admission to candidacy are: to have the student review and integrate his previous work, to allow the institution to check on the adequacy of the chosen course program and to determine if and what additional courses may be needed, and in some instances to determine at a relatively early stage that the candidate does not appear competent to continue towards completion of degree requirements. Oral comprehensive examinations are ordinarily short, with a primary function of determining ability to present and defend ideas. The oral thesis or dissertation defense is similar, but also important for judging the adequacy of the work.

6-6. TRAINING PROGRAMS. Organizational training programs are primarily intended to provide the link between the basic theory learned in college and the practical applications of that theory used in the specific industry. Advanced theoretical studies may be included in the program, particularly where formal graduate courses are not conveniently available for the employees. Certificates are usually given upon completion of the program and/or courses as an incentive and reward; these are usually presented at a ceremony and a copy placed in the personal file.

Historically, most early training programs initially assigned the graduate to the testing of company products and to assembly jobs, prior to shipment. These assignments gave the opportunity to examine critically and become familiar with company products. Assignments would move progressively from being an assistant in a test or assembly, to being in charge of a test or assembly where ability to lead a small number of employees could be observed. Further familiarity with the organization was obtained by transient assignments of up to three months in each of the divisions including those of production, design, research, safety, personnel, purchasing, sales, and field offices. Upon completion of the program it was assumed that the employee would be particularly able to choose a division for regular assignment, and to work thereafter cooperatively with the other divisions.

Comprehensive training programs today may extend over the full period of the working life of the employee and include the following parts or aspects:

a) Initial orientation to procedures, policies, personnel, objectives, company history and organization, products, services, and customer relations;

b) Transient work assignments in each of the various divisions;

c) Lectures on fundamentals and their correlation to the organizations' products or services;

d) Specialized training for the regular assignment;

e) Advanced technical and related studies, including engineering writing, on a continuing basis or periodically when major changes in products or services take place—these may be done by released time a few hours per week or by concentrated company seminars, workshops or symposiums;

f) Creative engineering program to develop intuitive abilities —this may involve an apprenticeship under engineers with proven creative abilities supplemented by classroom training a few hours per week to go over fundamentals of engineering and their applications to proposed changes or new designs;

g) Supervisory and managerial training;

h) Testing of employees' grasp of the subject matter and experiences presented in the training program;

i) Encouragement and support of registration and professional activities outside of the organization including professional engineering examination refresher courses, assistance in preparation of papers for publication and in carrying out duties of offices in professional societies, and subsidies for professional society dues and attendance at regional and national conventions.

6-7. EVALUATION OF THE EDUCATIONAL SYSTEM.

Accreditation of engineering curricula is participated in by members of the profession in general practice as well as by those in the educational function. This joint responsibility recognizes that the engineering schools exist to serve the practice of engineering and must ever be alert to meet its changing needs. The alumni of each school or college of engineering have an obligation to evaluate continuously in the light of their own experience and to make suggestions to the faculty; and through the professional societies worthwhile ideas can be communicated to all other educational institutions. Changes in the educational system are usually, and should be, made slowly after due deliberation, so that one should not expect their suggestions to be followed until sufficient support of others is obtained and the matter is passed upon by committees and agencies of each educational institution. Evaluation of the primary and secondary public school systems is a further obligation which can be implemented through P.T.A., other organizations, and also the local chapters of the professional societies.

The evaluation of education appears to be very much a function of the particular position and age of the individual doing the evaluating. The young graduate will tend to feel that more emphasis should be placed upon the technical subjects, while the older engineer who has moved into a position which is primarily administrative will tend to feel that more emphasis should be placed upon the humanities, social studies, and business management courses. The engineer performing research will tend to feel that more emphasis should be placed upon mathematics and basic science, while the engineer performing specialized design will tend to feel that more emphasis should be placed upon advanced engineering courses in his specialty. The engineer in a large industry with its own formal training program will tend to feel that emphasis should be upon broad background with relatively little attention paid to current engineering practice, while the engineer who is a principal in a small consulting office will tend to feel that the young graduate should be ready to move into current engineering practice with relatively little formal training on the job. The educational system must do its best to meet all these diverse needs. It is therefore important that young and old, employees of both large and small organizations, and engineers representative of all the functions be continuously heard, lest one or more elements create an improper balance in the system.

Numerous problems are being faced by the educational system at any one time—many still relatively unresolved after years of consideration. New facts, new ideas, new approaches to old problems are vitally needed. Some of the problem areas of engineering education which many believe need further consideration are:

(1) How many years should be required for the first degree in engineering?

(2) How much humanities and social studies should be required and where should these be taught (e.g., entirely in the secondary school, as in Europe)?

(3) What is the optimum class size in the light of burgeoning enrollments? Can television solve the problem?

(4) Should beginning courses in classical physics be taught by the engineering or physics faculty?

(5) Should graduate engineering curricula be accredited?

(6) To what extent should Federal aid to education be accepted?

(7) Is the emphasis on graduate programs and research grants causing neglect of the undergraduate curricula?

(8) To what extent should there be a common core of subjects for majors in all fields of engineering? for majors in engineering and the physical sciences?

(9) Should graduate engineering education be administered by the Dean of Engineering or by the Dean of the Graduate School?

(10) Can creativity be taught at the undergraduate level?

(11) Should professional ethics be taught by example or precept?

(12) How can more engineering technicians be obtained to relieve the graduate engineers of routine tasks?

(13) Should engineering technicians be taught in separate institutions, or can the first two years in the engineering school be used as a primary base?

(14) Should the Master's degree be required for engineering registration, and the Bachelor's degree be considered the minimum requirement for engineering technicians?

(15) Is the quality of graduate instruction seriously lowered when given in off-campus centers?

ASSIGNMENTS

6.1 Discuss your plans and reasoning for your personal continuation of education, after graduation.

6.2 Make a critical analysis of what you consider to have been the major strengths and weaknesses in the curricula, faculty, and organization of your engineering school.

SUGGESTED ADDITIONAL READING

BERELSON, BERNARD. *Graduate Education in the United States.* New York: McGraw-Hill Book Company, Inc., 1960. 346 pp.

CARMICHAEL, OLIVER C. *Graduate Education.* New York: Harper & Brothers, 1961. 213 pp.

Facilities and Opportunities for Graduate Study in Engineering. Urbana, Illinois: American Society for Engineering Education, 1958. 37 pp.

NESS, FREDERIC W., editor, *A Guide to Graduate Study.* 2nd ed.; Washington, D. C.: American Council on Education, 1960. 457 pp.

The Unwritten Laws of

Engineering * *by* W. J. KING

Part 1 WHAT THE BEGINNER NEEDS TO LEARN

AT ONCE

Some years ago the author became very much impressed with the fact, which can be observed in any engineering organization, that the chief obstacles to the success of individual engineers or of the group comprising a unit were of a personal and administrative rather than a technical nature. It was apparent that both the author and his associates were getting into much more trouble by violating the unwritten laws of professional conduct than by committing technical sins against the well-documented laws of science. Since the former appeared to be indeed unwritten at that time, as regards any adequate and convenient text, the following "laws" were originally formulated and collected into a sort of scrapbook, to provide a set of "house rules," or a professional code, for a design-engineering section of a large manufacturing organization. Although they are admittedly fragmentary and incomplete, they are offered here for whatever they may be worth to younger men just starting their careers, and to older men who know these things perfectly well but who all too often fail to apply them in practice.

Just a few points should be emphasized: None of these "laws" is

* Reprinted by permission from the May, June, and July, 1944 issues of *Mechanical Engineering*.

theoretical or imaginary, and however obvious and trite they may appear, their repeated violation is responsible for much of the frustration and embarrassment to which engineers everywhere are liable. In fact this paper is primarily a record, derived from direct observation over a period of seventeen years, of the experience of four engineering departments, three of them newly organized and struggling to establish themselves by the trial-and-error method. It has, however, been supplemented and confirmed by the experience of others as gathered from numerous discussions, lectures, and the literature, so that it most emphatically does not reflect the unique experience or characteristics of any one organization.

Furthermore, many of these rules are generalizations to which exceptions will occur in special circumstances. There is no thought of urging a slavish adherence to rules and red tape, for there is no substitute for judgment, and at times vigorous individual initiative is needed to cut through formalities in an emergency. But in many respects these laws are like the basic laws of society; they cannot be violated too often with impunity, notwithstanding striking exceptions in individual cases.

IN RELATION TO HIS WORK

However menial and trivial your early assignments may appear give them your best efforts. Many young engineers feel that the minor chores of a technical project are beneath their dignity and unworthy of their college training. They expect to prove their true worth in some major enterprise. Actually, the spirit and effectiveness with which you tackle your first humble tasks will very likely be carefully watched and may affect your entire career.

Occasionally a man will worry unduly about where his job is going to get him—whether it is sufficiently strategic or significant. Of course these are pertinent considerations and you would do well to take some stock of them, but by and large it is fundamentally true that if you take care of your present job well, the future will take care of itself. This is particularly so in the case of a large corporation, where executives are constantly searching for competent men to move up into more responsible positions. Success depends so largely upon personality, native ability, and vigorous, intelligent prosecution of any job that it is no exaggeration to say that your ultimate chances are much better if you do a good job on some minor detail than if you do a mediocre job as section head. Furthermore, it is also true that if you do not first make a good showing on your present job you are not likely to be given the opportunity of trying something else more to your liking.

There is always a premium upon the ability to get things done.
This is a quality which may be achieved by various means under
different circumstances. Specific aspects will be elaborated in some of
the succeeding items. It can probably be reduced, however, to a combination of three basic characteristics, as follows:

(*a*) Energy which is expressed in initiative to start things and aggres-
siveness to keep them moving briskly.

(*b*) Resourcefulness or ingenuity, i.e., the faculty for finding ways to
accomplish the desired result, and

(*c*) Persistence (tenacity), which is the disposition to persevere in
spite of difficulties, discouragement, or indifference.

This last quality is sometimes lacking in the make-up of brilliant
engineers, to such an extent that their effectiveness is greatly reduced.
Such dilettantes are known as "good starters but poor finishers." Or
else it will be said of a man: "You can't take him too seriously; he'll
be all steamed up over an idea today but tomorrow he will have
dropped it and started chasing some other rainbow." Bear in mind,
therefore, that it may be worth while finishing a job, if it has any
merit, just for the sake of finishing it.

*In carrying out a project do not wait for foremen, vendors, and
others to deliver the goods; go after them and keep everlastingly after
them.* This is one of the first things a new man has to learn in entering
a manufacturing organization. Many novices assume that it is sufficient
to place the order and sit back and wait until the goods are delivered.
The fact is that most jobs move in direct proportion to the amount
of follow-up and *expediting* that is applied to them. Expediting means
planning, investigating, promoting, and facilitating every step in the
process. Cultivate the habit of looking immediately for some way
around each obstacle encountered, some other recourse or expedient
to keep the job rolling without losing momentum. There are ten-to-
one differences between individuals in respect to what it takes to stop
their drive when they set out to get something done.

On the other hand, the matter is occasionally overdone by over-
zealous individuals who make themselves obnoxious and antagonize
everyone by their offensive browbeating tactics. Be careful about de-
manding action from another department. Too much insistence and
agitation may result in more damage to a man's personal interest than
could ever result from the miscarriage of the technical point involved.

*Confirm your instructions and the other fellow's commitments in
writing.* Do not assume that the job will be done or the bargain kept
just because the other fellow agreed to do it. Many people have poor
memories, others are too busy, and almost everyone will take the matter

a great deal more seriously if he sees it in writing. Of course there are exceptions, but at times it pays to mark a third party for a copy of the memo, as a witness.

When sent out on any complaint or other assignment stick with it and see it through to a successful finish. All too often a young engineer from the home office will leave a job half done or poorly done in order to catch a train or keep some other engagement. Wire the boss that you've got to stay over to clean up the job. Neither he nor the customer will like it if another man has to be sent out later to finish it up.

Avoid the very appearance of vacillation. One of the gravest indictments of an engineer is to say: "His opinion at any time depends merely upon the last man with whom he has talked." Refrain from stating an opinion or promoting an undertaking until you have had a reasonable opportunity to obtain and study the facts. Thereafter see it through if at all possible, unless fresh evidence makes it folly to persist. Obviously the extremes of bullheadedness and dogmatism should be avoided, but remember that reversed decisions will be held against you.

Don't be timid—speak up—express yourself and promote your ideas. Every young man should read Emerson's essay on "Self Reliance." Too many new men seem to think that their job is simply to do what they're told to do, along the lines laid down by the boss. Of course there are times when it is very wise and prudent to keep your mouth shut, but, as a rule, it pays to express your point of view whenever you can contribute something. The quiet mousey individual who says nothing is usually credited with having nothing to say.

It frequently happens in any sort of undertaking that nobody is sure of just how the matter ought to be handled; it's a question of selecting some kind of program with a reasonable chance of success. This is commonly to be observed in engineering-office conferences. The first man to speak up with a definite and plausible proposal has better than an even chance of carrying the floor, provided only that the scheme is definite and plausible. (The "best" scheme usually cannot be recognized as such in advance.) It also happens that the man who talks most knowingly and confidently about the matter will very often end up with the assignment to carry out the project. If you do not want the job, keep your mouth shut and you'll be overlooked, but you'll also be overlooked when it comes time to assign larger responsibilities.

Before asking for approval of any major action, have a definite plan and program worked out to support it. Executives very generally and very properly will refuse to approve any proposed undertaking that is not well planned and thought through as regards the practical details of its execution. Quite often a young man will propose a project without having worked out the means of accomplishing it, or weighing the actual advantages against the difficulties and costs. This is the difference between a "well-considered" and a "half-baked" scheme.

Strive for conciseness and clarity in oral or written reports. If there is one bane of an executive's existence, it is the man who takes a half hour of rambling discourse to tell him what could be said in one sentence of twenty words. There is a curious and widespread tendency among engineers to surround the answer to a simple question with so many preliminaries and commentaries that the answer itself can hardly be discerned. It is so difficult to get a direct answer out of some men that their usefulness is thereby greatly diminished. The tendency is to explain the answer before answering the question. To be sure, very few questions admit of simple answers without qualifications, but the important thing is to state the crux of the matter as succinctly as possible first. On the other hand, there are times when it is very important to add the pertinent background or other relevant facts to illuminate a simple statement. The trick is to convey the maximum of significant information in the minimum time, a valuable asset to any man.

An excellent guide in this respect may be found in the standard practice of newspapers in printing the news. The headlines give 90 per cent of the basic facts. If you have the time and the interest to read further, the first paragraph will give you most of the important particulars. Succeeding paragraphs simply give details of progressively diminishing significance. To fit an article into available space, the editor simply lops off paragraphs from the rear end, knowing that relatively little of importance will be lost. You can hardly do better than to adopt this method in your own reports, presenting your facts in the order of importance, as if you might be cut off any minute.

Be extremely careful of the accuracy of your statements. This seems almost trite, and yet many engineers lose the confidence of their superiors and associates by habitually guessing when they do not know the answer to a direct question. It is certainly important to be able to answer questions concerning your responsibilities, but a wrong answer is worse than no answer. If you do not know, say so, but also say, "I'll find out right away." If you are not certain, indicate the exact degree of certainty or approximation upon which your answer is based. A reputation for dependability and reliability can be one of your most valuable assets.

This applies, of course, to written matter, calculations, etc., as well as to oral reports. It is definitely bad business to submit a report to the boss for approval without first carefully checking it yourself, and yet formal reports are sometimes turned in full of glaring errors and omissions.

IN RELATION TO THE BOSS

Every executive must know what's going on in his bailiwick. This principle is so elementary and fundamental as to be axiomatic. It follows from the very obvious fact that a man cannot possibly manage his business successfully unless he knows what's going on in it. It applies to minor executives and other individuals charged with specific responsibilities as well as to department heads. No one in his right mind will deny the soundness of the principle and yet it is very commonly violated or overlooked. It is cited here because several of the rules which follow are concerned with specific violations of this cardinal requirement.

Do not overlook the fact that you're working for your boss. This sounds simple enough, but some engineers never get it. By all means, you're working-for society, the company, the department, your family, and yourself, but primarily you should be working for and through your boss. And your boss is your immediate superior, to whom you report directly. As a rule, you can serve all other ends to best advantage by working for him, assuming that he's approximately the man he ought to be. It is not uncommon for young engineers, in their impatient zeal to get things done, to ignore the boss, or attempt to go over or around him. Sometimes they move a little faster that way, for a while, but sooner or later they find that such tactics cannot be tolerated in a large organization. Generally speaking, you cannot get by the boss; he determines your rating and he rates you on your ability to co-operate, among other things. Besides, most of us get more satisfaction out of our jobs when we're able to give the boss our personal loyalty, with the feeling that we're helping him to get the main job done.

Be as particular as you can in the selection of your boss. In its effect upon your engineering career, this is second in importance only to the selection of proper parents. In most engineering organizations the influence of the senior engineer, or even the section head, is a major factor in molding the professional character of younger engineers. Long before the days of universities and textbooks, master craftsmen in all the arts absorbed their skills by apprenticeship to master craftsmen. It is very much as in the game of golf; a beginner who constantly plays in company with "dubs" is very apt to remain a "dub" himself, no matter how faithfully he studies the rules, whereas even a few rounds with a "pro" will usually improve a novice's game.

But, of course, it is not always possible to choose your boss advisedly. What if he turns out to be somewhat less than half the man he ought to be? There are only two proper alternatives open to you; *(a)* accept him as the representative of a higher authority and execute his policies and directives as effectively as possible, or *(b)* transfer to some other outfit at the first opportunity. A great deal of mischief can be done to the interests of all concerned (including the company) if some other alternative is elected, particularly in the case of younger men. Consider the damage to the efficiency of a military unit when the privates, disliking the leader, ignore or modify orders to suit their individual notions! To be sure, a business organization is not a military machine, but it is not a mob, either.

One of the first things you owe your boss is to keep him informed of all significant developments. This is a corollary of the preceding rules: An executive must know what's going on. The main question is: How much must he know—how many of the details? This is always a difficult matter for the new man to get straight. Many novices hesitate to bother the boss with too many reports, and it is certainly true that it can be overdone in this direction, but in by far the majority of cases the executive's problem is to extract enough information to keep adequately posted. For every time he has to say, "Don't bother me with so many details," there will be three times he will say, "Why doesn't someone tell me these things?" Bear in mind that he is constantly called upon to account for, defend, and explain your activities to the "higher-ups," as well as to co-ordinate these activities into a larger plan. In a nutshell, the rule is therefore to give him promptly all the information he needs for these two purposes.

Whatever the boss wants done takes top priority. You may think you have more important things to do first, but unless you obtain permission it is usually unwise to put any other project ahead of a specific assignment from your own boss. As a rule, he has good reasons for wanting his job done *now,* and it is apt to have a great deal more bearing upon your rating than less conspicuous projects which may appear more urgent.

Also, make a note of this: If you are instructed to do something and you subsequently decide it isn't worth doing (in view of new data or events) do not just let it die, but inform the boss of your intentions and reasons. Neglect of this point has caused trouble on more than one occasion.

Do not be too anxious to follow the boss's lead. This is the other side of the matter covered by the preceding rule. An undue subservience or deference to the department head's wishes is fairly common among young engineers. A man with this kind of psychology may:

1 Plague the boss incessantly for minute directions and approvals.

2 Surrender all initiative and depend upon the boss to do all of his basic thinking for him.

3 Persist in carrying through a design or a program even after new evidence has proved the original plan to be wrong.

This is where an engineering organization differs from an army. In general, the program laid down by the department or section head is tentative, rather than sacred, and is intended to serve only until a better program is proposed and approved.

This rule therefore is to tell your boss what you have done, at reasonable intervals, and ask his approval of any well-considered and properly planned deviations or new projects that you may have conceived.

REGARDING RELATIONS WITH ASSOCIATES AND OUTSIDERS

Never invade the domain of any other division without the knowledge and consent of the executive in charge. This is a very common offense, which causes no end of trouble. Exceptions will occur in respect to minor details, but the rule applies particularly to:

1 The employment of a subordinate. Never offer a man a job, or broach the matter at all, without first securing the permission of his boss. There may be excellent reasons why the man should not be disturbed.

2 Engaging the time or committing the services of a subordinate for some particular project or trip. How would you feel, after promising in a formal meeting to assign one of your men to an urgent project, to discover that some other executive had had the gall to send him on an out-of-town trip without attempting to notify you? Yet it has been done!

3 Dealings with customers or outsiders, with particular reference to making promises or commitments involving another division. In this connection bear in mind especially that, when you are in the "field" or the "districts," you are in the premises of the district manager or local office, and that all transactions must be with the manager's permission just as if you were in his home.

4 Performing any function assigned to another division or individual. Violations of this law often cause bitter resentments and untold mischief. The law itself is based upon three underlying principles:

(a) Most people strongly dislike having anyone "muscle" into their territory, undermining their job by appropriating their functions.

(b) Such interference breeds confusion and mistakes. The man in charge of the job usually knows much more about it than you do, and, even when you think you know enough about it, the chances are better than even that you'll overlook some important factor.

(c)   Nine times out of ten when you're performing the other fellow's function you're neglecting your own. It is rarely that any engineer or executive is so caught up on his own responsibilities that he can afford to take on those of his colleagues.

There is a significant commentary on this last principle which should also be observed: In general you will get no credit or thanks for doing the other fellow's job for him at the expense of your own. But it frequently happens that, if you can put your own house in order first, an understanding of and an active interest in the affairs of other divisions will lead to promotion to a position of greater responsibility. Many a man has been moved up primarily because of a demonstrated capacity for taking care of other people's business as well as his own.

In all transactions be careful to "deal-in" everyone who has a right to be in. It is extremely easy, in a large corporation, to overlook the interests of some division or individual who does not happen to be represented, or in mind, when a significant step is taken. Very often the result is that the step has to be retracted or else considerable damage is done. Even when it does no apparent harm, most people do not like to be left out when they have a stake in the matter, and the effect upon morale may be serious.

Of course there will be times when you cannot wait to stand on ceremony and you'll have to go ahead and "damn the torpedoes." But you cannot do it with impunity too often.

Note particularly that in this and the preceding item the chief offense lies in the invasion of the other man's territory without his knowledge and consent. You may find it expedient on occasions to do the other man's job for him, in order to get your own work done, but you should first give him a fair chance to deliver the goods or else agree to have you take over. If you must offend in this respect, at least you should realize that you are being offensive.

Be careful about whom you mark for copies of letters, memos, etc., when the interests of other departments are involved. A lot of mischief has been caused by young men broadcasting memoranda containing damaging or embarrassing statements. Of course it is sometimes difficult for a novice to recognize the "dynamite" in such a document but, in general, it is apt to cause trouble if it steps too heavily upon someone's toes or reveals a serious shortcoming on anybody's part. If it has wide distribution or if it concerns manufacturing or customer difficulties, you'd better get the boss to approve it before it goes out unless you're very sure of your ground.

Promises, schedules, and estimates are necessary and important instruments in a well-ordered business. Many engineers fail to realize this, or habitually try to dodge the irksome responsibility for making commitments. You *must* make promises based upon your own estimates for the part of the job for which you are responsible, together with estimates obtained from contributing departments for their parts. No one should be allowed to avoid the issue by the old formula, "I can't give a promise because it depends upon so many uncertain factors." Consider the "uncertain factors" confronting a department head who must make up a budget for an entire engineering department for a year in advance! Even the most uncertain case can be narrowed down by first asking, "Will it be done in a matter of a few hours or a few months—a few days or a few weeks? It usually turns out that it cannot be done in less than three weeks and surely will not require more than five, in which case you'd better say four weeks. This allows one week for contingencies and sets you a reasonable bogie under the comfortable figure of five weeks. Both extremes are bad; a good engineer will set schedules which he can meet by energetic effort at a pace commensurate with the significance of the job.

As a corollary of the foregoing, you have a right to insist upon having estimates from responsible representatives of other departments. But in accepting promises, or statements of facts, it is frequently important to make sure that you are dealing with a properly qualified representative of the other section. Also bear in mind that when you ignore or discount another man's promises you impugn his responsibility and incur the extra liability yourself. Of course this is sometimes necessary, but be sure that you do it advisedly. Ideally, another man's promises should be negotiable instruments, like his personal check, in compiling estimates.

When you are dissatisfied with the services of another section, make your complaint to the individual most directly responsible for the function involved. Complaints made to a man's superiors, over his head, engender strong resentments and should be resorted to only when direct appeal fails. In many cases such complaints are made without giving the man a fair chance to correct the grievance, or even before he is aware of any dissatisfaction.

This applies particularly to individuals with whom you are accustomed to deal directly or at close range, or in cases where you know the man to whom the function has been assigned. It is more formal and in some instances possibly more correct to file a complaint with the head of a section or department, and it will no doubt tend to secure prompt results. But there are more than a few individuals who would never forgive you for complaining to their boss without giving them a fair chance to take care of the matter.

Next to a direct complaint to the top, it is sometimes almost as serious an offense to mark a man's boss for a copy of a letter containing a complaint or an implied criticism. Of course the occasion may justify such criticism; just be sure you know what you're doing.

In dealing with customers and outsiders remember that you represent the company, ostensibly with full responsibility and authority. You may be only a few months out of college but most outsiders will regard you as a legal, financial, and technical agent of your company in all transactions, so be careful of your commitments.

Part 2   RELATING CHIEFLY TO

ENGINEERING EXECUTIVES

The following is a partial list of basic commandments, readily subscribed to by all executives but practiced only by the really good ones:

INDIVIDUAL BEHAVIOR AND TECHNIQUE

Every Executive must know what's going on in his bailiwick. This is repeated here for emphasis, and because it belongs at the head of the list for this section. Just remember that it works both ways, as regards what you owe your associates and subordinates as well as yourself.

Obviously this applies primarily to major or significant developments and does not mean that you should attempt to keep up with all the minor details of functions assigned to subordinates. It becomes a vice when carried to the extent of impeding operations. Nevertheless, the basic fact remains that the more information an executive has, the more effectively he can manage his business.

Do not try to do it all yourself. This is another one of those elementary propositions that everyone will endose and yet violations are quite common. It's *bad* business; bad for you, bad for the job, and bad for your men. You *must* delegate responsibility even if you *could* cover all of the ground yourself. It isn't wise to have so much depend upon one man and it's very unfair to your men. It is often said that every executive should have his business so organized that he could take a month's vacation at any time and have everything go along smoothly. The most common excuse for hogging the whole job is that subordinates are too young or inexperienced. It's part of your job to develop your men, which includes developing initiative, resourcefulness, and judgment. The best way to do this is to load them up with all the responsibility they can carry without danger of serious embarrassment to the department. Any self-respecting engineer resents being babied, to the extent where he cannot act on the most trivial detail without express approval of the department head.

On the other hand, it must be granted that details are not always trivial and it may sometimes require a meeting of the management committee to change the length of a screw in a critical piece of mechanism in high production. It's simply a matter of making sure that all items are handled by men of appropriate competence and experience.[1]

Put first things first, in applying yourself to your job. Since there usually isn't time for everything, it is essential to form the habit of concentrating on the important things first. The important things are the things for which you are held directly responsible and accountable, and if you aren't sure what these are you'd better find out mighty quick and fix them clearly in mind. Assign these responsibilities top priority in budgeting your time; then delegate as many as possible of the items which will not fit into your schedule: It is a good general rule never to undertake any minor project or chore that you can get someone else or some other department to do for you, so long as it is not an essential part of your job. For example, if your job is building motors it's a mistake to spend time designing special vibration or sound meters for testing them if you can get the laboratory to do it for you.

In handling special problems of this sort, it is usually good diplomacy to let some local office do the job, if they can, before importing experts from another plant or company.

The practice of drawing upon all available resources for assistance can frequently be applied to advantage in respect to your major products, as well as in minor details. This is especially true in a large organization where the services of experts, consulting engineers, laboratories, and other departments are available either at no cost or for much less than it would cost you to get the answer independently. In fact, there may well be cases in which it would be wise for you to limit yourself, personally or as a business manager, to performing only those functions to which you can bring some special talent, skill, or contribution, or in which you enjoy some natural advantage. Some companies, for example, have achieved outstanding success by virtue of their special genius for merchandising the products of others, or by concentrating on the manufacture of a standard competitive article so as to capture the market by lowering the price. Likewise the aircraft

[1] "Administrative Organization for a Small Manufacturing Firm," by Willis Rabbe, MECHANICAL ENGINEERING, vol. 63, 1941, pp. 517–520.

companies generally exploit their special aeronautical skill, leaving development of engines, superchargers, propellers, and other components to specialists in these fields. Few of us are versatile enough to excel in more than one or two talents.

Cultivate the habit of "boiling matters down" to their simplest terms. The faculty for reducing apparently complicated situations to their basic, essential elements is a form of wisdom that must usually be derived from experience, but there are marked differences between otherwise comparable individuals in this respect. Some people seem eternally disposed to "muddy the water;" or they "can never see the woods for the trees," etc. Perhaps a man cannot correct such an innate tendency simply by taking thought, but it appears to be largely a matter of habit, a habit of withdrawing mentally to a suitable vantage point so as to survey a mass of facts in their proper perspective, or a habit of becoming immersed and lost in a sea of detail. Make it a practice to integrate, condense, summarize, and simplify your facts rather than to expand, ramify, complicate, and disintegrate them.

Many meetings, for example, get nowhere after protracted wrangling until somebody finally says, "Well, gentlemen, it all boils down simply to this, . . .", or "Can't we agree, however, that the basic point at issue is just this, ...", or, "After all the essential fact remains that . . . ."

This sort of mental discipline, which instinctively impels a man to go down to the core to get at the crux of the matter, is one of the most valuable qualities of a good executive.[2]

Do not get excited in engineering emergencies—keep your feet on the ground. This is certainly trite enough, and yet an engineering group will sometimes be thrown into a state of agitation bordering on panic by some minor crisis. This refers especially to bad news from the factory or the field regarding some serious and embarrassing difficulty, such as an epidemic of equipment failures. Most crises aren't half as bad as they appear at first, so make it a point to minimize rather than magnify a bad situation. Do not ignore signs of trouble and get caught napping, but learn to distinguish between isolated cases and real epidemics. The important thing is to get the facts first, as promptly and as directly as possible. Then act as soon as you have enough evidence from responsible sources to enable you to reach a sound decision.

Engineering meetings should not be too large or too small. Many executives carry their aversion for large meetings to the point of a phobia. This is reflected in the common saying that nothing worth while is ever accomplished in a large meeting. It is true enough that large meetings frequently dissipate the subject over a number of con-

[2] See also: "Psychology for Executives," by Elliott Dunlap Smith, Harper & Brothers, New York, N. Y., 1935.

flicting or irrelevant points of view, in a generally superficial manner. But this is almost entirely a matter of the competence of the chairman. A considerable amount of skill is required to manage a sizable meeting so as to keep it on the proper subject, avoiding long-winded digressions or reiterations of the arguments. It should be the function of the chairman, or the presiding senior executive, to bring out the pertinent facts bearing upon the matter, in their logical order, and then to secure agreement upon the various issues by (a) asking for general assent to concrete proposals, or (b) taking a vote, or (c) making arbitrary decisions. Engineering meetings may degenerate into protracted wrangles for lack of competent direction. The danger in this respect seems to be about in proportion to the size of the meeting.

Small meetings, three or four persons, can usually hammer out a program or dispose of knotty problems much more effectively. The chief drawback lies in the possibility that all interested parties may not be represented, and considerable loss or mischief may result from failure to take account of significant facts or points of view. Apart from the actual loss involved, strong resentment or discouragement may be engendered in the neglected parties. (The Revolutionary War was brought about largely as a result of the fact that the Colonies were not represented in the British Parliament.)

There will doubtless be cases in which it is neither feasible nor desirable to have all interested parties represented in engineering discussions, particularly if the participants are well informed. But in general it is fitting, proper, and helpful to have the man present whose particular territory is under discussion.

An excellent expedient for avoiding the objections to either extreme in this respect is to keep the meeting small, calling in each keyman when his particular responsibility is being discussed.

In any kind of a meeting the important thing is to face the issues and dispose of them. All too often there is a tendency to dodge the issues, postponing action until a later date, or "letting the matter work itself out naturally." Matters will always work out "naturally" if the executive function of control is neglected but this represents a low order of "management." Count any meeting a failure which does not end up with a definite understanding as to what's going to be done; who's going to do it, and when. This should be confirmed in writing (minutes).

Cultivate the habit of making brisk, clean-cut decisions. This is, of course, the most difficult and important part of an executive's job. Some executives have a terrific struggle deciding even minor issues, mainly because they never get over being afraid of making mistakes. Normally, facility comes with practice, but it can be hastened by observing a few simple principles.

1   Decisions will be easier and more frequently correct if you have the essential facts at hand. It will therefore pay you to keep well informed, or else to bring out the relevant facts before attempting a decision. However, it is sometimes said that anybody can make decisions when all of the facts are at hand, whereas an executive will make the same decisions without waiting for the facts.[3] To maintain a proper balance in this respect, when in doubt ask yourself the question: "Am I likely to lose more by giving a snap judgment or by waiting for more information?"

2   The application of judgment can be facilitated by formulating it into principles, policies, and precepts in advance. The present paper is an attempt to formulate experience for this purpose. Make up your own code, if you will, but at least have some sort of code, for much the same reason that you memorize the axioms of Euclid or Newton's laws of motion.

3   You do not have to be right every time. It is said that a good executive needs to be right only 51 per cent of the time (although a little better margin would obviously be healthy).

4   The very fact that a decision is difficult usually means that the advantages and drawbacks of the various alternatives are pretty well balanced, so that the net loss cannot amount to much in any event. In such cases it is frequently more important to arrive at some decision —any decision—promptly than to arrive at the best decision ultimately. So take a definite position and see it through.

5   It is futile to try to keep everybody happy in deciding issues involving several incompatible points of view. By all means give everyone a fair hearing, but after all parties have had their say and all facts are on the table, dispose of the matter decisively even if someone's toes are stepped on. Otherwise the odds are that all parties will end up dissatisfied, and even the chief beneficiary will think less of you for straddling the issue.

The following criteria are helpful in choosing a course of action when other factors are indecisive; ask yourself these questions:

(a)   Does it expedite and progress the undertaking, or does it smack of procrastination and delay?

(b)   Is it fair and square and aboveboard?

(c)   Is it in line with established custom, precedence of policy? A good reason is generally required for a departure.

(d)   Is it in line with a previous specific decision or understanding?

[3] See "Definition of an Executive," by H. S. Osborne, *Electrical Engineering*, vol. 61, August, 1942, p. 429.

Even a good reason for making a change will sometimes not offset the unfortunate impression of apparent instability. "He can't make up his own mind" is a common reaction. (Observe, however, that this criterion is suggested only "when other factors are indecisive." By all means have the courage of your convictions when the change is justifiable.)

(e) What are the odds? Can I afford to take the chance? How does the possible penalty compare with the possible gain, in each of the alternatives offered? Very often you can find a solution wherein the worst possible eventually isn't too bad, in relation to the possible gains.

Do not allow the danger of making a mistake to inhibit your initiative to the point of "nothing ventured, nothing gained." It is much healthier to expect to make mistakes, take a few good risks now and then, and take your medicine when you lose. Moreover, there are few mistakes that cannot be turned into profit somehow, even if it's only in terms of experience.

Finally, it should be observed that having "the courage of your convictions" includes having the courage to do what you know to be right, technically as well as morally, without undue regard for possible criticism or the necessity for explaining your actions. Many seemingly embarrassing situations can readily be cleared up, or even turned to advantage, merely by stating the simple, underlying facts of the matter. It boils down to a very straightforward proposition: If your reasons for your actions are sound, you should not worry about having to defend them to anyone; if they're not sound you'd better correct them promptly, instead of building up an elaborate camouflage.

Do not overlook the value of suitable "preparation" before announcing a major decision or policy. When time permits, it is frequently good diplomacy to prepare the ground for such announcements by discussing the matter in advance with various keymen or directly interested parties. This is, in fact, an elementary technique in diplomatic and political procedure, but it is all too often ignored in engineering practice. Much embarrassment and bad feeling can be caused by announcing a major change or embarking upon a new program or policy without consulting those directly affected or who are apt to bring up violent objections, with good reason later on.[4]

HANDLING DESIGN AND DEVELOPMENT PROJECTS

Beware of the "perils of security" in planning your enginering programs. It is one of the fundamental anomalies of human experience

[4] See also: "The Technique of Executive Control," by Erwin Haskell Schell. Fifth edition, McGraw-Hill Book Co., Inc., New York, N. Y., 1942.

that too much preoccupation with the pursuit of security is very apt to lead to greater danger and insecurity. In a competitive world you *must* take chances—bold and courageous chances—or else the other fellow will, and he will win out just often enough to keep you running, all out of breath, trying to catch up. So it behooves you as an engineering executive to "stick your neck out," and keep it out, by undertaking stiff development programs, setting a high mark to shoot at, and then working aggressively to realize your objectives. With competent direction any representative engineering organization will work its way out of a tight spot, every time, under the pressure of the emergency. If you do not like such "emergencies," just remember that, if you do not create your own emergencies in advance, your competition will create them for you at a much more embarrassing time later on.

In order to miminize the risk it is good policy to hedge against the failure of a new project by providing an alternative, or an "out" to fall back on, wherever practicable. You can go after bigger stakes with impunity when you have suitably limited your possible losses in such a manner.

Plan your work, then work your plan. The following formula for carrying out a development or design project seems to be standard in the best engineering circles:

(*a*) Define your objectives.
(*b*) Plan the job, by outlining the steps to be accomplished.
(*c*) Prepare a definite schedule.
(*d*) Assign definite responsibilities for each item.
(*e*) Make sure that each man has sufficient help and facilities.
(*f*) Follow up; check up on progress of the work.
(*g*) Revise your schedule as required.
(*h*) Watch for "bottlenecks," "log-jams," and "missing links;" hit lagging items hard.
(*i*) Drive to a finish on time.

Plan your development work far enough ahead of production so as to meet schedules without a wild last-minute rush. In the nature of things it seems inevitable that the group responsible for design engineering is also in the best position to take care of development projects. This is due to the intimate contacts of the designers with the practical problems of production, performance, and market requirements. But it is also true that very considerable foresight is required to offset the natural tendency of designers to become preoccupied with immediate problems of this nature, at the expense of the long-range development program, which is not so urgent and pressing. It is therefore the function of management to exercise sufficient "vision" to anticipate trends and initiate research and development projects before the demand becomes uncomfortably urgent. This means starting such projects soon enough, i.e., six months, a year, or even two years in advance, to allow sufficient time to carry out all the necessary steps in a well-ordered program.

Even when the development of new designs simply means a rehash of old fundamentals in new dress, it is important to plan the program early enough and to provide for all stages in the process of getting the product on the market. For example, the following steps may be required to carry through the development of a typical peacetime product:

(a) Market survey.
(b) Preparation of commercial specifications (features and ratings agreed upon jointly by commercial and design divisions).
(c) Preliminary designs.
(d) Build and test preliminary sample.
(e) Final design.
(f) Build and test final samples.
(g) Preliminary planning and costs.
(h) Engineering release of final drawings for production.
(i) Final planning and costs.
(j) Ordering materials and tools.
(k) Preparation of manufacturing and test instructions, application, installation, operating and service manuals, replacement-parts catalogue, publicity releases.
(l) Initial production.
(m) Test production samples.
(n) Minor design changes to correct errors and expedite production.

Obviously, some of these activities can be carried on concurrently, but unless they are all suitably provided for there is very apt to be some awkward stumbling and bungling along the way.

Be careful to "freeze" a new design when the development has progressed far enough. Of course it is not always easy to say how far is "far enough" but, in general, you have gone far enough when you can meet the design specifications and costs, with just enough time left to complete the remainder of the program on schedule. The besetting temptation of the designing engineer is to allow himself to be led on by one glittering improvement after another, pursuing an elusive perfection that leads him far past the hope of ever keeping his promises and commitments. Bear in mind that there will always be new design improvements coming along, but it is usually better to get started with what you have on time, provided only that it is up to specifications as regards features, quality, and cost.

Constantly review developments and other activities to make certain that actual benefits are commensurate with costs in money, time, and manpower. Not infrequently developments are carried along by virtue of Newton's first law of motion long after they have ceased to yield a satisfactory return on the investment. The occasion for vigilance in this respect is obvious enough; it is cited here simply as a reminder.

Make it a rule to require, and submit, regular periodic progress reports, as well as final reports on completed projects. However irksome such chores may seem, your business simply isn't fully organized and controlled until you have established this practice, as regards reports to your superiors as well as from your subordinates. There appears to be no other regimen quite so compelling and effective in requiring a man to keep his facts properly assembled and appraised.

It is further true that, generally speaking, an engineering project is not really finished until it is properly summarized, recorded, and filed in such a manner that the information can readily be located and utilized by all interested parties. An enormous amount of effort can be wasted or duplicated in any engineering department when this sort of information is simply entrusted to the memory of individual engineers.

NOTES RESPECTING ORGANIZATION[5]

Do not have too many men reporting directly to one man. As a rule, not more than six or seven men should report to one executive in an engineering organization. Occasionally a strong energetic leader will deal directly with fifteen or twenty engineers, in which case he is usurping the positions and functions of several group leaders, burdening himself with too much detail, and depriving the men of adequate supervision.

Assign definite responsibilities. It is extremely deterimental to morale and efficiency when no one knows just what his job is or what he is responsible for. If assignments are not made clear there is apt to be interminable bickering, confusion, and bad feeling. Do not keep tentative organization changes hanging over people. It is better to dispose of a situation promptly, and change it later, than to hold up a decision simply because you might want to change it. It is again a matter of facing issues squarely; it is easier to "just wait and see how things work

---

[5] For a more authoritative discussion of this subject, see the excellent series of papers on "Organization and Management of Engineering," *Electrical Engineering,* vol. 61, Aug., 1942, pp. 422–429.

out" but, beyond the minimum time required to size up personnel, it's not good management.

In so far as possible, avoid divided responsibility for specific functions. Ideally each man should have full authority and control over all of the factors essential to the performance of his particular function. This is commonly expressed in the aphorism that authority must be commensurate with responsibility. In practice this is seldom possible of fulfillment; we must all depend upon the contributions of others at some point in the process. Still the amount of dependency should be kept to the practical minimum, for it is extremely difficult for a man to get anything done if he must eternally solicit the voluntary co-operation or approval of too many other parties. This is what is known as being "organized to prevent things from getting done."

The logical answer to the problem of divided responsibility (or "division of labor") is co-ordination. If any activity, such as the design of a product, must be divided into development, design, drafting, and production engineering, these functions should obviously be co-ordinated by a single responsible engineer.

If you haven't enough legal authority assume as much as you need. During the Civil War a Confederate officer one evening found that his supply train was held up by a single Union battery which was dropping shells accurately into a narrow mountain pass. Without even changing his uniform, he rode around to the rear of the battery, and, coming upon them suddenly, sharply ordered them to swing their guns around to another point. He was obeyed with alacrity because he acted as if he expected to be obeyed. He rode off to rejoin his command, and led them through the pass before anyone discovered that he had exceeded his authority.

Of course such tactics are not recommended for general use, but the story illustrates the fact that quite a lot can be accomplished, on occasions, without full administrative sanction. The important thing is to exercise sufficient care to avoid running afoul of the interests and authority of others.

This injunction is based upon three elementary facts of experience:

1 A man will frequently be held responsible for a good deal more than he can control by directly delegated authority.

2 A very considerable amount of authority can be assumed with complete impunity if it is assumed discreetly, and with effective results. People in general tend to obey a man who appears to be in charge of any situation, provided that he appears to know what he is doing and obtains the desired results.

3 Most executives will be pleased to confirm such authority in their subordinates when they see it being exercised effectively. Executives

in general have much more trouble pushing their men ahead than in holding them back.

Do not create "bottlenecks." Co-ordination of minor routine affairs is sometimes carried too far, when a single individual must pass upon each transaction before it can be carried out. Such rigid control can easily cause more trouble than the original liability. Fortunately, bottlenecks are usually recognized early in the game, and it is easy to avoid them by designating alternates, or by allowing freedom of action in emergencies, with the proviso that the proper party be notified at the first opportunity.

Assign responsibilities for technical subjects, as well as for specific products, in setting up your engineering organization. This is a practice which could be used to advantage in design sections more frequently than it is. The idea is to assign dual responsibilities to each engineer; (*a*) for a particular product or line of apparatus, and (*b*), for a technical specialty, such as lubrication, heat transfer, surface finishes, magnetic materials, welding, fluid flow, etc. These assignments should be made known to all members of the group, with the request that all pertinent material on each subject be referred to the proper specialist, who will act as consultant and as contact man with laboratories, etc., for the entire section. It may, of course, be desirable to assign full-time specialists to important subjects when the business can afford it; the main point is to establish pools of specialized knowledge rather than to expect each designer to know all that he needs to know about the principal arts and sciences which are common to the various products of the department.

WHAT EVERY EXECUTIVE OWES HIS MEN

Promote the personal and professional interests of your men on all occasions. This is not only an obligation, it is the opportunity and the privilege of every executive.

As a general principle, the interests of individual engineers coincide with the company's interest, i.e., there is, or should be, no basic conflict. The question of which should be placed first is, therefore, rarely encountered in practice, although it is clear that, in general, the company's interests, like those of the state or society, must take precedence. It is one of the functions of management to reconcile and merge the two sets of interests to their mutual advantage, since they are so obviously interdependent.

It should be obvious that it is to the company's advantage to preserve the morale and loyalty of individual engineers, just as it is common policy to maintain proper relations with the labor unions.

The fact is that attempts to organize engineers into unions have failed simply because the engineers have been confident that their interests have been looked after very conscientiously and very adequately by responsible executives.

Morale is a tremendously important factor in any organization. It is founded primarily upon confidence, and it reaches a healthy development when the men feel that they will always get a square deal plus a little extra consideration on occasions.

Specific injunctions under this principle are cited in succeeding items.

Do not hang onto a man too selfishly when he is offered a better opportunity elsewhere. It's a raw deal to stand in the way of a man's promotion just because it will inconvenience you to lose him. You are justified in shielding him from outside offers only when you are sincerely convinced that he has an equal or better opportunity where he is. Moreover, you should not let yourself get caught in a position where the loss of any man would embarrass you unduly. Select and train runners-up for all keymen, including yourself.

Do not short-circuit or override your men if you can possibly avoid it. It is very natural, on occasions, for an executive to want to exercise his authority directly in order to dispose of a matter promptly without regard for the man assigned to the job. To be sure, it's your prerogative, but it can be very demoralizing to the subordinate involved and should be resorted to only in real emergencies. Once you give a man a job, let him do it, even at the cost of some inconvenience to yourself. Never miss a chance to build up the prestige of your men. And more than a little mischief can be done by exercising authority without sufficient knowledge of the details of the matter.

You owe it to your men to keep them properly informed. Next to responsibility without authority comes responsibility without information, in the catalogue of raw deals. It is very unfair to expect a man to acquit himself creditably when he is held responsible for a project without adequate knowledge of its past history, present status, or future plans. An excellent practice, followed by many top-flight executives, is to hold occasional meetings of section heads to acquaint them with major policies and developments in the business of the department and the company, so that all will know what's going on.

An important part of the job of developing a man is to furnish him with an ample background of information in his particular field, and as a rule this involves a certain amount of travel. There are occasions when it is worth while to send a young man along on a trip for what he can get out of it, rather than what he can contribute to the job.

Do not criticize one of your men in front of others, especially his own subordinates. This obviously damages prestige and morale.

Also, be very careful not to criticize a man when it's really your own fault. Not infrequently, the real offense can be traced back to you, as when you fail to advise, or warn, or train the man properly. Be fair about it.

Show an interest in what your men are doing. It is definitely discouraging to a man when his boss manifests no interest in his work, as by failing to inquire, comment, or otherwise take notice of it.

Never miss a chance to commend or reward a man for a job well done. Remember that your job is not just to criticize and browbeat your men into getting their work done. A first-rate executive is a leader as well as a critic. The better part of your job is, therefore, to help, advise, encourage, and stimulate your men.

On the other hand, this does not mean mollycoddling. By all means get tough when the occasion justifies it. An occasional sharp censure, when it is well deserved, will usually help to keep a man on his toes. But if that's all he gets, he is apt to go a bit sour on the job.

Always accept full responsibility for your group and the individuals in it. Never "pass the buck" or blame one of your men, even when he has "let you down" badly, in dealings with outsiders. You are supposed to have full control and you are credited with the success as well as the failure of your group.

Do all that you can to see that each of your men gets all of the salary that he's entitled to. This is the most appropriate reward or compensation for outstanding work, greater responsibility, or increased value to the company. (Any recommendation for an increase in salary must be justified on one of these three bases.)

Include interested individuals in introductions, luncheons, etc., when entertaining visitors. Obviously, this can be overdone, but if you're entertaining a visiting specialist, it is good business, as well as good manners, to invite the corresponding specialist in your own department to go along.

Do all that you can to protect the personal interests of your men and their families, especially when they're in trouble. Do not confine your interest in your men rigidly within the boundaries of "company business."

Try to get in little extra accommodations when justifiable. For example, if you're sending a man to his home town on a business trip, schedule it for Monday, so that he can spend Sunday with his family, if it makes no difference otherwise.

Considerations of this sort make a "whale" of a difference in the matter of morale and in the satisfaction an executive gets out of his job. The old-fashioned "slave driver" is currently regarded in about the same light as Heinrich Himmler. Treat your men as human beings making up a team rather than as cogs in a machine.

In this connection, it is sometimes advisable to talk things over with a man when you become definitely dissatisfied with his work, or recognize a deficiency which is militating against him. To be sure, it is not always easy, and may require much tact to avoid discouraging or offending the man, but it may well be that you owe it to him. Bear this in mind; if you ultimately have to fire him, you may have to answer two pointed questions: "Why has it taken you five years to discover my incompetence?" and, "Why haven't you given me a fair chance to correct these shortcomings?" Remember that when you fire a man for incompetence, it means not only that he has failed, but also that you have failed.

Part 3   PURELY PERSONAL CONSIDERATIONS

FOR ENGINEERS

The importance of the personal and sociological aspects of our behavior as engineers is brought out in the following quotation (1):[1]

"In a recent analysis of over 4000 cases, it was found that 62 per cent of the employees discharged were unsatisfactory because of social unadaptability, only 38 per cent for technical incompetence."

And yet about 99 per cent of the emphasis in the training of engineers is placed upon purely technical or formal education. In recent years, however, there has been a rapidly growing appreciation of the importance of "human engineering," not only in respect to relations between management and employees but also as regards the personal effectiveness of the individual worker, technical or otherwise. It should be obvious enough that a highly trained technological expert with a good character and personality is necessarily a better engineer and a great deal more valuable to his company than a sociological freak or misfit with the same technical training. This is largely a consequence of the elementary fact that in a normal organization no individual can get very far in accomplishing any worth-while objectives without the voluntary co-operation of his associates; and the quantity and quality of such co-operation is determined by the "personality factor" more than anything else.

This subject of personality and character is, of course, very broad and much has been written and preached about it from the social,

[1] Numbers in parentheses refer to the Bibliography at the end of the paper.

ethical, and religious points of view. The following "laws" are drawn up from the purely practical point of view based upon well-established principles of "good engineering practice," or upon consistently repeated experience. As in the preceding sections, the selections are limited to rules which are frequently violated, with unfortunate results, however obvious or bromidic they may appear.

"LAWS" OF CHARACTER AND PERSONALITY

One of the most important personal traits is the ability to get along with all kinds of people. This is rather a comprehensive quality but it defines the prime requisite of personality in any type of industrial organization. No doubt this ability can be achieved by various formulas, although it is probably based mostly upon general, good-natured friendliness, together with fairly consistent observance of the "Golden Rule." The following "do's and don'ts" are more specific elements of such a formula:

1 Cultivate the tendency to appreciate the good qualities rather than the shortcomings of each individual.

2 Do not give vent to impatience and annoyance on slight provocation. Some offensive individuals seem to develop a striking capacity for becoming annoyed, which they indulge with little or no restraint.

3 Do not harbor grudges after disagreements involving honest differences of opinion. Keep your arguments on an objective basis and leave personalities out as much as possible.

4 Form the habit of considering the feelings and interests of others.

5 Do not become unduly preoccupied with your own selfish interests. It may be natural enough to "look out for Number One first," but when you do your associates will leave the matter entirely in your hands, whereas they will be much readier to defend your interests for you if you characteristically neglect them for unselfish reasons.

This applies particularly to the matter of credit for accomplishments. It is much wiser to give your principal attention to the matter of getting the job done, or to building up your men, than to spend too much time pushing your personal interests ahead of everything else. You need have no fear of being overlooked; about the only way to lose credit for a creditable job is to grab for it too avidly.

6 Make it a rule to help the other fellow whenever an opportunity arises. Even if you're mean-spirited enough to derive no personal satisfaction from accommodating others it's a good investment. The business world demands and expects co-operation and teamwork among the members of an organization. It's smarter and pleasanter to give it freely and ungrudgingly, up to the point of unduly neglecting your own responsibilities.

7 Be particularly careful to be fair on all occasions. This means a good deal more than just being fair, upon demand. All of us are frequently unfair, unintentionally, simply because we do not habitually view the matter from the other fellow's point of view, to be sure that his interests are fairly protected. For example, when a man fails to carry out an assignment, he is sometimes unjustly criticized when the real fault lies with the executive who failed to give him the tools to do the job. Whenever you enjoy some natural advantage, or whenever you are in a position to injure someone seriously, it is especially incumbent upon you to "lean over backwards" to be fair and square.

8 Do not take yourself or your work too seriously. A normal healthy sense of humor, under reasonable control, is much more becoming, even to an executive, than a chronically soured dead-pan, a perpetually unrelieved air of deadly seriousness, or the pompous solemn dignity of a stuffed owl. The Chief Executive of the United States smiles easily or laughs heartily, on appropriate occasions, and even his worst enemies do not attempt to criticize him for it. It is much better for your blood pressure, and for the morale of the office, to laugh off an awkward situation now and then than to maintain a tense tragic atmosphere of stark disaster whenever matters take an embarrassing turn. To be sure, a serious matter should be taken seriously, and a man should maintain a quiet dignity as a rule, but it does more harm than good to preserve an oppressively heavy and funereal atmosphere around you.

9 Put yourself out just a little to be genuinely cordial in greeting people. True cordiality is, of course, spontaneous and should never be affected, but neither should it be inhibited. We all know people who invariably pass us in the hall or encounter us elsewhere without a shadow of recognition. Whether this be due to inhibition or preoccupation we cannot help feeling that such unsociable chumps would not be missed much if we never saw them again. On the other hand, it is difficult to think of anyone who is too cordial, although it can doubtless be overdone like anything else. It appears that most people tend naturally to be sufficiently reserved or else over-reserved in this respect.

10 Give the other fellow the benefit of the doubt if you are inclined to suspect his motives, especially when you can afford to do so. Mutual distrust and suspicion breed a great deal of absolutely unnecessary friction and trouble, frequently of a very serious nature. This is a very common phenomenon, which can be observed among all classes and types of people, in international as well as local affairs. It is derived chiefly from misunderstandings, pure ignorance, or from an ungenerous tendency to assume that a man is guilty until he is proved

innocent. No doubt the latter assumption is the "safer" bet, but it is also true that if you treat the other fellow as a depraved scoundrel, he will usually treat you likewise, and he will probably try to live down to what is expected of him. On the other hand you will get much better co-operation from your associates and others if you assume that they are just as intelligent, reasonable, and decent as you are, even when you know they're not (although the odds are 50:50 that they are). It isn't a question of being naïve or a perpetual sucker; you'll gain more than you lose by this practice, with anything more than half-witted attention to the actual odds in each case.

Do not be too affable. It's a mistake, of course, to try too hard to get along with everybody merely by being agreeable and friendly on all occasions. Somebody will take advantage of you sooner or later, and you cannot avoid trouble simply by running away from it ("appeasement"). You must earn the respect of your associates by demonstrating your readiness to give any man a hell of a good fight if he asks for it. Shakespeare put it succinctly in Polonius' advice to his son (in "Hamlet"): "Beware of entrance to a quarrel; but being in, bear it that the opposed may beware of thee."

On the other hand, do not give ground too quickly just to avoid a fight, when you know you're in the right. If you can be pushed around easily the chances are that you will be pushed around. There will be times when you would do well to start a fight yourself, when your objectives are worth fighting for.

As a matter of fact, as long as you're in a competitive business you're in a fight all the time. Sometimes it's a fight between departments of the same company. As long as it's a good clean fight, with no hitting below the belt, it's perfectly healthy. But keep it on the plane of "friendly competition" as long as you can. (In the case of arguments with your colleagues, it is usually better policy to settle your differences out of court, rather than to take them to the boss for arbitration.)

Likewise, in your relations with subordinates it is unwise to carry friendliness to the extent of impairing discipline. There are times when the best thing that you can do for a man (and the company) is to fire him, or transfer him. Every one of your men should know that whenever he deserves a good "bawling out" he'll get it, every time. The most rigid discipline is not resented so long as it is reasonable, impartial, and fair, especially when it is balanced by appropriate rewards, appreciation, and other compensations as mentioned in Part 2. Too much laxity or squeamishness in handling men is about as futile as cutting off a dog's tail an inch at a time to keep it from hurting so much. If you do not face your issues squarely, someone else will be put in your place who will.

Regard your personal integrity as one of your most important assets. In the long pull there is hardly anything more important to you than your own self-respect and this alone should provide ample incentive to maintain the highest standard of ethics of which you are capable. But, apart from all considerations of ethics and morals, there are perfectly sound hardheaded business reasons for conscientiously guarding the integrity of your character.

One of the most striking phenomena of an engineering office is the transparency of character among the members of any group who have been associated for any length of time. In a surprisingly short period each individual is recognized, appraised, and catalogued for exactly what he is, with far greater accuracy than that individual usually realizes. This is true to such a degree that it makes a man appear downright ludicrous when he assumes a pose or otherwise tries to convince us that he is something better than he is. As Emerson puts it: "What you are speaks so loud I cannot hear what you say." In fact it frequently happens that a man is much better known and understood by his associates, collectively, than he knows and understands himself.

Therefore, it behooves you as an engineer to let your personal conduct, overtly and covertly, represent your conception of the very best practical standard of professional ethics, by which you are willing to let the world judge and rate you.

Moreover, it is morally healthy and tends to create a better atmosphere, if you will credit the other fellow with similar ethical standards, even though you may be imposed upon occasionally. The obsessing and overpowering fear of being cheated is the common characteristic of second- and third-rate personalities. This sort of psychology sometimes leads a man to assume an extremely "cagey" sophisticated attitude, crediting himself with being impressively clever when he is simply taking advantage of his more considerate and fair-minded associates. On the other hand a substantial majority of top-flight executives are scrupulously fair, square, and straightforward in their dealings with all parties. In fact most of them are where they are largely because of this characteristic, which is one of the prime requisites of first-rate leadership.

The priceless and inevitable reward for uncompromising integrity is confidence, the confidence of associates, subordinates, and "outsiders." All transactions are enormously simplified and facilitated when a man's word is as good as his bond and his motives are above suspicion. Confidence is such an invaluable business asset that even a moderate amount of it will easily outweigh any temporary advantage that might be gained by sharp practices.

Integrity of character is closely associated with sincerity, which is another extremely important quality. Obvious and marked sincerity is frequently a source of exceptional strength and influence in certain individuals, particularly in the case of speakers. Abraham Lincoln is a classic example. In any individual, sincerity is always appreciated, and insincerity is quickly detected and discounted.

In order to avoid any misunderstanding, it should be granted here that the average man, and certainly the average engineer, is by no means a low dishonest scoundrel. In fact the average man would violently protest any questioning of his essential honesty and decency, perhaps fairly enough. But there is no premium upon this kind of common garden variety of honesty, which is always ready to compromise in a pinch. The average man will go off the gold standard or compromise with any sort of expediency whenever it becomes moderately uncomfortable to live up to his obligations. This is hardly what is meant by "integrity," and it is certainly difficult to base even a moderate degree of confidence upon the guarantee that you will not be cheated unless the going gets tough.

A little profanity goes a long way. Engineering is essentially a gentleman's profession, and it ill becomes a man to carry profanity to the point of becoming obnoxiously profane. Unfortunately, profanity is sometimes taken as a mark of rugged he-man virility, but any engineer with such an idea should realize that many a pimply, half-witted, adolescent street urchin will hopelessly outclass him in this respect.

On the other hand, there is no reason why a man should be afraid to say "damn." On appropriate occasions a good hearty burst of colorful profanity may be just a healthy expression of strong feelings. But there is never any occasion for the filthy variety of obscenity, and a really foul mouth will generally inspire nothing but contempt.

Be careful of your personal appearance. Roughly eight out of every ten engineers pay adequate attention to their personal appearance and neatness. The other two offend in respect to one or more of the following items:

1   Suit rumpled or soiled, or else trousers, coat, and vest have nothing in common but their means of support.

2   Shoes, unpolished or dilapidated.

3   Tie, at half-mast or looking like it was tied with one hand. Some individuals seem to own but one tie, which takes an awful beating. Others wear colors contrasting violently with suit or shirt, but this is sometimes a matter of artistic license (if it isn't color blindness).

4   Shirt, frayed at collar or cuffs, or just plain dirty.

5   Hands, dirty.

6   Nails, in deep mourning, chewed off, or else absurdly long. A

man doesn't need to be fastidious, but dirty neglected nails immediately and conspicuously identify a careless sloppy individual. (This is especially true in the case of an interview, where first impressions are so important.)

Of course we all know some very good men who are oblivious to such details, so that it cannot be said that all who ignore them are necessarily crude, third-rate, slovenly low-brows, but it is probably a safe bet that all crude, third-rate, slovenly low-brows are offensive in most of these respects.

Do not argue that you cannot afford to look your best; you cannot afford not to. Your associates and superiors notice these details, perhaps more than you realize, and they rate you accordingly.

In this connection, note the following quotation from a recent pamphlet on "employee rating" (2):

"The 'halo effect' simply means that rating of one trait is often influenced by that given to some other trait. Thus an employee who makes a nice appearance and has a pleasant manner is apt to obtain a higher rating on all other traits than he deserves."

Analyze yourself and your men. In the foregoing, it has been assumed that any normal individual will be interested in either:

(*a*) Advancement to a position of greater responsibility, or (*b*) improvement in personal effectiveness as regards quantity and/or quality of accomplishment.

Either of these should result in increased financial compensation and satisfaction derived from the job.

With reference to item (*a*), it is all too often taken for granted that increased executive and administrative responsibility is a desirable and appropriate form of reward for outstanding proficiency in any type of work. This may be a mistake from either of two points of view:

1 The individual may be very much surprised to find that he is much less happy in his new job than he thought he was going to be. In many instances young engineers are prone to assume that increased responsibility means mostly increased authority and compensation. Actually, the term "compensation" is well applied, for the extra salary is paid primarily to compensate for the extra burden of responsibility. Of course most people relish the added load, because of the larger opportunities that go with it, but many perfectly normal individuals find it more of a load than anything else. It is not uncommon for an engineer or a scientist to discover, to his dismay, that as soon as he becomes an executive he no longer has time to be an engineer or a scientist. In fact, some executives have time for absolutely nothing else.

2 From the business standpoint, it by no means follows that because a man is a good scientist, he will make a good executive.

Many a top-notch technician has been promoted to an administrative position very much to his own and the job's detriment.

These facts should therefore be considered carefully by the man threatened with promotion and by the man about to do the promoting. There are other ways of rewarding a man for outstanding accomplishment.

It is not always easy, however, to decide in advance whether you, or the man in question, would be happier and more effective as an executive or as an individual worker. There is no infallible criterion for this purpose but it will be found that, in general, the two types are distinguished by the characteristics and qualities listed in Table 1.

TABLE 1   CHARACTERISTIC QUALITIES FOR EXECUTIVE OR INDIVIDUAL WORKERS

Executive	*Individual worker*
Extrovert	Introvert
Cordial, affable	Reserved
Gregarious, sociable	Prefers own company
Likes people	Likes technical work
Interested in people	Interested in mechanisms, ideas
Interested in:	Interested in:
Business	Sciences
Costs	Mathematics
Profit and loss	Literature
Practices	Principles
Ability to get many things done	Ability to get intricate things done
Practical	Idealistic
Extensive (broad perspectives)	Intensive (penetrating)
Synthesist	Analyst
Fast, intuitive	Slow, methodical
Talent for leadership	Independent, self-sufficient
Uses inductive logic	Uses deductive logic
Has competitive spirit	Prefers to "live and let live"
Bold	Modest
Courageous	Retiring
Noisy	Quiet
Aggressive	Restrained
Tough, rugged	Vulnerable, sensitive
Confident	Deferential
Impulsive	Intellectual
Vigorous, energetic	Meditative, philosophical
Opinionated, intolerant	Broad-minded, tolerant
Determined	Adaptable
Impatient	Patient
Enterprising	Conservative

Of course many people represent intermediate types, or mixtures; the attributes given in Table 1 delineate the pronounced types. Nevertheless, if most of your attributes lie in the righthand column the chances are very much against your becoming a successful executive. On the other hand, if you are interested primarily in increasing your effectiveness as an individual worker you would do well to develop some of the strong qualities listed in the left column, to reinforce the virtues on the right.

Two facts stand out sharply in this connection:

1 Whatever your position, and however complacent you may be about it, there is always room for improving your effectiveness; usually plenty of room.

2 Whatever your natural handicaps may be, it is always possible to accomplish such improvement by study and practice, provided only that you have the will, the determination, and the interest to sustain the effort.

It is very much like the design of a piece of apparatus. Any experienced engineer knows that it is always possible to secure substantial improvements by a redesign. When you get into it you will find that there are few subjects more absorbing or more profitable than the design and development of a good engineer! As Alexander Pope wrote many years ago:

"The proper study of mankind is man."

As previously suggested, this applies to the development of your men as well as yourself. It likewise applies to the appraisal and selection of men. After your own character, the next most important factor in your ultimate success is the caliber of your assistants. In fact, there are, doubtless, cases where the character of the executive is not particularly important, provided only that he is smart enough to surround himself with top-notch men to carry the load. In many instances the success or failure of your business will depend upon whether your engineers are slightly above or below the marginal level of competence for the industry.

It is a significant fact that, in the overwhelming majority of cases, the decisive differences in the abilities of engineers are relatively small. In spite of the occasional incidence of a genius or nit-wit, the great majority of personnel in any industry and the backbone of the large organizations are individuals who vary only slightly from the norm. In general, when executives look over an organization to select a man for a better job, those who are passed up have very few actual shortcomings, but the man who is chosen has the least. Likewise, many top executives are distinguished not so much by marked genius as by relative freedom from defects of character. There is nowhere near enough genius to go around.

This should be particularly heartening to the younger men who view the leaders of industry with awe and wonder upon what meat they feed. Nine out of ten of you have "what it takes" as regards native endowments. The problem is to make the most of what you have.

To this end it will be helpful to study some of the employee rating sheets and charts that have been evolved by various industries. Sample forms and a general discussion of the subject will be found in the pamphlet on "employee rating" (2). It is very noticeable that most of these forms are concerned chiefly with acquired rather than inherited traits. The point is that most of the features upon which individuals are rated represent bad habits or plain ignorance, i.e., features that may be controlled and corrected by conscious effort.

CONCLUSION

The foregoing "laws" represent only one basic element in the general formula for a successful engineering career. The complete list of essential components is as follows:

(a)   The written laws (the arts and sciences).

(b)   The unwritten laws, of which the foregoing is admittedly no more than a preliminary and very inadequate summary.

(c)   Native endowments (intelligence, imagination, health, energy, etc.)

(d)   Luck, chance, opportunities ("the breaks").

The last item is included because good or bad fortune undoubtedly enters into the picture occasionally. Broadly speaking, however, luck tends to average out at a common level over a period of years, and there are more opportunities looking for men than there are men looking for opportunities.

About all that we can do about our native endowments is to conserve, develop, and utilize them to best advantage.

The "unwritten laws," including those that are still unwritten, are needed to give direction to our efforts in this latter respect.

The "written laws" receive plenty of attention during our formal schooling, but our studies are not always extended as effectively as they might be after graduation. In many cases, superior technical knowledge and training represents the marginal consideration in the selection of men for key positions.

To anyone interested in improving his professional effectiveness, further study of both types of laws will yield an excellent return on the investment. Under present conditions, however, most engineering graduates are much closer to the saturation point in respect to the written than to the unwritten variety. A few references are listed in the Bibliography for the benefit of those who may be interested in further excursions into these subjects.

Finally it should be observed that the various principles which have been expounded, like those of the arts and sciences, must be assiduously applied and developed in practice if they are to become really effective assets. It is much easier to recognize the validity of these "laws" than it is to apply them consistently, just as it is easier to accept the doctrines of Christianity than to practice them. The important thing here is to select, in so far as possible, a favorable atmosphere for the development of these professional skills. This is undoubtedly one of the major advantages of employment in a large engineering organization, just as it is advantageous to a young doctor to spend his internship in the Mayo Clinic. Perhaps even more important, as previously mentioned, is the selection of your boss, particularly during those first few years that constitute your engineering apprenticeship. No amount of precept is as effective as the proper kind of example. Unfortunately, there is not nearly enough of this kind of example to go around, and in any event it will behoove you to study the "rules of the game" to develop your own set of principles to guide you in your professional practice.

BIBLIOGRAPHY

1 "Elements of Human Engineering," by C. R. Gow, Macmillan Company, New York, N. Y., 1932.
2 "Employee Rating," National Industrial Conference Board, Report 39, New York, N. Y., 1942.
3 "Papers on the Science of Administration," by Luther Gulick and L. Urwick, Institute of Public Administration, Columbia University, New York, N. Y., 1937 (New York State Library, Albany, reference 350.1, qG97).
4 "Principles of Industrial Organization," by D. S. Kimball, McGraw-Hill Book Company, Inc., New York, N. Y., 1933.
5 "Organization and Management in Industry and Business," by W. B. Cornell, The Ronald Press, New York, N. Y., 1936.
6 "Industrial Management," by R. H. Lansburgh and W. R. Spriegel, third edition, John Wiley & Sons, Inc., New York, N. Y., 1940.
7 "The Functions of the Executive," by Chester I. Barnard, Harvard University Press, Cambridge, Mass., 1938.
8 "Human Relations Manual for Executives," by Carl Heyel, McGraw-Hill Book Company, Inc., New York, N. Y., 1939.
9 "Organization and Management of Engineering Described at

Unusual General Session," reviewing by M. R. Sullivan, R. C. Muir, and H. B. Gear, *Electrical Engineering*, vol. 61, August, 1942, pp. 422-429.

10 "Administrative Organization for a Small Manufacturing Firm," by Willis Rabbe, MECHANICAL ENGINEERING, vol. 63, 1941, pp. 517-520.

11 "Task of the Executive in Modern Industry," by John Airey, *Journal of Engineering Education,* vol. 32, Jan., 1942, pp. 472-479.

12 "Middle Management," by Mary Cushing Howard Niles, Harper & Bro., New York, N. Y., 1941.

13 "Management's Handbook," by L. P. Alford, The Ronald Press Company, New York, N. Y., 1924.

14 "Shop Management," by F. W. Taylor, Harper & Bro., New York, N. Y., 1911. (This is a classic work in which Taylor is credited with laying the foundations of modern "scientific management.")

15 "Onward Industry," by J. D. Mooney and A. C. Reily, Harper & Bro., New York, N. Y., 1931.

16 "Personnel Management and Industrial Relations," by Dale Yoder, Prentice-Hall, Inc., New York, N. Y., 1942.

17 "Industrial Psychology," by Joseph Tiffin, Prentice-Hall, Inc., New York, N. Y., 1942.

18 "Industrial Psychology, Industrial Relations," by Irving Knickerbocker, MECHANICAL ENGINEERING, vol. 65, 1943, pp. 137-138.

19. "What Men Live By," by R. C. Cabot, Houghton-Mifflin Company, New York, N. Y., 1914.

20 "Psychology for Business and Industry," by Herbert Moore, McGraw-Hill Book Company, Inc., New York, N. Y., 1939.

21 "Industrial Management," by G. G. Anderson, M. J. Mandeville, and J. M. Anderson, The Ronald Press Company, New York, N. Y., 1943.

22 "Psychology for Executives," by E. D. Smith, Harper & Bro., New York, N. Y., 1935.

23 "Industrial Relations Handbook," by J. C. Aspley and E. Whitmore, The Dartnell Corporation, Chicago, Ill., 1943.

24 "The Technique of Executive Control," by Erwin Haskell Schell, fifth edition, McGraw-Hill Book Company, Inc., New York, N. Y., 1942.

25 "Management of Manpower," by A. S. Knowles and R. D. Thomson, Macmillan Company, New York, N. Y., 1943.

Supplementary Definitions for Use in Ethical Discourse*

ANGER—*the desire whereby, through hatred, we are induced to injure someone or something which we hate.*

APPETITE—*An impulse or endeavor to modify the body and/or mind.* See also *Desire* and *Will.*

APPROVAL—*love towards one who has done good to another or towards something considered good.* See also *Indignation.*

AVARICE—*the excessive desire and love of riches.*

BEAUTY—*a measure of the capacity to give pleasure.*

BENEVOLENCE—*the desire to do good for others.*

CONCEIT—*the attributing to oneself of a perfection which is not there.*

CONFIDENCE—*pleasure arising from an idea wherefrom cause of doubt as to the issue has been removed.* See also *Despair.*

COURTESY—*the desire to act in a way which should please men, and refraining from that which should displease them.*

COWARDICE—*the checking of desire by the fear of some danger which others, who are equal, dare to encounter.*

CRUELTY—*the desire whereby a man is impelled indifferently to injure other beings.*

DESIRE—*a conscious impulse or endeavor to modify the body and/or mind.* See also *Appetite* and *Will.*

DESPAIR—*pain arising from an idea wherefrom cause of doubt as to the issue has been removed.* See also *Confidence.*

DEVOTION—*love toward something which we admire or respect.*

* See §3-3 for basic definitions.

DISAPPOINTMENT—*pain accompanied by the idea of something past, which has had an issue contrary to our hope.* See also *Joy.*

DISPARAGEMENT—*hatred in so far as it induces a man to injure by unfavorable comparison.*

DUTY—*the conduct or action required of a person by ethical considerations.*

EMOTION—*the modifications of the body whereby the active power of the body, and the ideas of such modifications, are increased or diminished.*

EMULATION—*the desire to equal or surpass another.*

ENVY—*hatred, in so far as it induces a man to be distressed by another's good fortune, and to rejoice in another's evil fortune.* See also *Sympathy.*

EVIL—*that which, in accordance with reason, is a hindrance to us in the attainment of any good.*

FATALISM—*the doctrine that all events are irrevocably predetermined so that human efforts cannot alter them.* See also *Free-will.*

FEAR—*an inconstant pain arising from the idea of something past or future, whereof we to a certain extent doubt the issue.* See also *Hope.*

FREE-WILL—*the doctrine that man has the power to choose between alternatives, without necessary compulsion of circumstances or motive.* See also *Fatalism.*

GRATITUDE—*the desire whereby we endeavor to benefit others who with similar feelings of love have conferred a benefit on us.*

GRIEF—*pain arising from contemplation of some good we have lost with no hope of recovering the same.*

HABIT—*a relatively fixed mode of activity developed by repetition.*

HATRED—*pain, accompanied by the idea of an external cause.* See also *Love.*

HONESTY—*the intent to act in accordance with truth and justice.*

HONOR—*pleasure accompanied by the idea of some action of our own, which we believe to be approved by others.* See also *Shame.*

HOPE—*an inconstant pleasure, arising from the idea of something past or future, whereof we do not yet know the issue.* See also *Fear.*

IDEA—*a mental conception.*

IDEAL—*a concept of an ultimate good, as developed by reason.*

IMAGINATION—*an idea of things not present to the physical senses.*

INDIGNATION—*hatred towards one who has done injury to another, or towards something considered evil.* See also *Approval.*

INTENT—*the purpose of an endeavor.*

JOY—*pleasure accompanied by the idea of something past, which has had an issue beyond our hope.*

LOVE—*pleasure accompanied by the idea of an external cause.* See also *Hatred.*

LUXURY—*excessive desire or possessions.*

MOTIVE—*that which prompts an endeavor.*

POLITICS—*an endeavor to build a social structure in which there will be the greatest harmony between man, applications of justice, and commanding positions occupied by the intellectually elite.*

REPENTANCE—*pain acompanied by the idea of one's self as cause.*

REVENGE—*the desire whereby we are induced to injure one who has injured us.*

SELF-APPROVAL—*pleasure arising from a man's contemplation of himself and his own power of action.*

SHAME—*pain acompanied by the idea of some action of our own, which we believe to be disapproved by others.* See also *Honor.*

SYMPATHY—*love, in so far as it induces a man to feel pleasure at another's good fortune and pain at another's evil fortune.* See also *Envy.*

TIMIDITY—*the fear whereby a man is induced to avoid an evil by encountering a lesser evil.*

WILL—*a conscious endeavor to modify the mind.* See also *Appetite* and *Desire.*

WONDER—*the conception of anything, wherein the mind comes to a stand, because the particular concept has no connection with other concepts.*

Index